D1612483

THE RIVER AND THE ROAD

The River and the Road

Journal of a Freshwater Pearl-fisher

by

PETER JAMES GOODWIN

ROBERT HALE · LONDON

First published in Great Britain 1985

ISBN 0 7090 2341 3

Robert Hale Limited
Clerkenwell House
Clerkenwell Green
London EC1R 0HT

British Library Cataloguing in Publication Data

Goodwin, Peter James
The river and the road : journal of a freshwater pearl-fisher.
1. Pearl-fisheries—Scotland
I. Title
639'.21'0924 SH377.G7

ISBN 0-7090-2341-3

Photoset in North Wales by
Derek Doyle & Associates, Mold, Clwyd.
Printed in Great Britain by
St Edmundsbury Press, Bury St Edmunds, Suffolk.
and bound by WBC Bookbinders Limited.

Contents

Illustrations

Photographs

between pages 136 and 137

Line drawings

PICTURE CREDITS

Photographs 1 and 2, *The Countryman*; 6, 7 and 8 D. Wilson Laing; all other photographs and drawings by the author.

Foreword

In a good autobiography in which a man declares his passion, it is not always what the author writes, but what he does not, that makes you want to know more. And Peter Goodwin's *The River and the Road* raised plenty of talking points in my mind. So it came about I drove to Perthshire and sought him out in a lonely cottage where he lives with his wife Nancy and nine-year-old Sarah Jane.

Until I read Peter's book I knew next to nothing about the natural history of the pearl mussel and the people who fished for them. Nor did I realize that the only markets for buying and selling are in Scotland and Scandinavia. At twenty-three years of age Peter didn't know very much either, but it was a television film about pearl-fishing which took him north from England to Scotland complete with tent, sleeping-bag, fiddle and banjo, guitar and autoharp.

His book took him three years to write, in a council house with the television set going in the room most of the time. Putting down his thoughts, he discovered, produced the same kind of stimulus as pearl-fishing, in that he never knew what he was going to come up with. He put it to me this way. "You feel you are in control when you sit down at the typewriter, but you don't know the country ahead. It's like riding a horse that takes off."

Now, at thirty-seven, Peter looks back in this book to his apprentice days when he was "accepted" by the folk whose attitude to life is that "Security" is a road to nowhere, and whose pearl-fishing equipment was as simple as their life style. These true professionals were hard nuts who made plenty of money from pearls but spent their earnings as they got them, never thinking of tomorrow.

These kindly folk opened their doors to him, and living with them Peter, the ex-university student, found utter fulfilment where in conventional life in England he had felt buried and punching at the air. Utterly careless of personal possessions he saw them as winners of freedom: pearl-fishers first, but labourers in the raspberry fields as a last resort.

Pearl-fishing can be hard. After many years in fierce rivers that chilled you to the bone for five or six hours at a stretch, he has discovered that your body never gets used to it. Here is one of many fine pieces of description:

> Heavy streams are exhausting to fish. Forward motion is akin to walking on ice cubes into a hurricane. Bent double over the jug, face close to the surface, the noise fills your head like an express train in a tunnel, and the water races beneath so wildly you feel as if you're looking through the hull of a glass-bottomed speed-boat. The effort of holding the jug racks the muscles, and the tangs are held clear of the water for this reason, and to allow two hands to be used to guide the jug. The wake the jug makes causes bubbles to travel under the glass and confuse the eye, or else it sweeps over it and almost snatches it from your grasp ... the feeling of relief when you reach quiet water is marvellous.

It was in a water like this, the fast-flowing River Spey, that one of his pearl-fishing friends drowned, a family man, the father of twins who had given up his work as a slater to become a professional pearl-fisher. The accident happened in June 1975. The unfortunate man was only 27, the same age as Peter at the time, and 'the boys' as he calls his fishing companions were using the Spey because their nearer bread-and-butter rivers were being fished to death by weekend pearlers and skin-divers.

Peter himself has not given up pearl-fishing, and if his writing is successful, he will use the money earned to cross the Atlantic and try his luck in some American rivers where little exploration has been done. And of course if he is lucky, the place where he will sell the spoils is Perth. I certainly wish him luck, good prices, and some more entertaining and informed writing on the subject closest to his heart.

For him peace and deep content can be found beyond the extremes of physical hardship when the prize is pearls requiring all he has to give to get the 'shells' out from the river bed into his bag.

Tom Weir

Introduction

Amongst the rubbish on the table beside my typewriter is a little leather pouch. It contains a couple of dozen Scottish river pearls, some of the nicest I found in the last year or two as a professional freshwater pearl-fisher and kept because soon I may never see their like again. They are not the kind of pearls you can buy in London, let alone a High Street jeweller's. They may be found in only two or three jewellers in north-east Scotland, and mainly in Perth.

Most people that my friends and I meet are surprised to know that freshwater pearls of great beauty have been fished from the rivers of Britain's hill country for over three thousand years. They are even more surprised to find that, up till very recently, a few pearl-fishers took a good, if precarious, living from the once rich mussel beds. For over ten years, two of these men, Donald McGregor and Neil McCormick, have been my friends and fishing companions.

Every so often, I open the pouch of pearls and pour them into my palm. I know them all well. I know the rivers they came from; I know the place where I sat opening the mussels they came from; I remember the weather, who came with us that day, and the lie of the hills around. What day, or even what year, it was may have been forgotten.

Gazing at their soft lustre, I can't help looking beyond them to other days, other rivers and other pearls, each with something, an incident or accident, to remind me of it. Can it be only ten years my friends and I had together? If it was such a short time, and so close behind us, why does it feel as if so many years have passed and that everything good is behind me now? So much happened in this short space that it has the air of the reminiscences of an old man waiting for the end, and whose friends, so seldom seen, have gone before him.

My friends, Donald McGregor and Neil McCormick of Rattray, Perthshire, taught me their ancient craft and shared the stories, legends and language of it with me till they became such a part of my life that my English origins were largely ignored by most people. Without what they gave me, I couldn't have written this book.

1. Discovery

Although I was born in early post-war Liverpool, less than thirty miles from the nearest pearl mussels in the River Dee, and although it was twenty-three years before I met with them in the rivers of South Devon, a strange link exists between these times. My mother often took me, as a child, by train to visit her sister in North Wales. I monopolized the window, scouring the countryside for every river or tiny stream. I couldn't let the best ones pass without drawing my mother's attention to them, nudging her if she was dozing. Something about the way they rippled between the fringe of trees lining their banks and wandered along the valleys fascinated me.

From the age of twelve I was brought up in Surrey. I lost my Liverpool accent and acquired what my friend Donald was to call 'a brute's accent', or a 'bool* in the mooth' manner of speech. I went through the motions of swimming with the stream: school, work, college, university, dropping out, then work again. All the time an undercurrent of subversive influences pulled me into as yet uncharted waters. Contrary to his intentions, my father was responsible for this. Somehow, while trying to persuade me to accept a 'leg up' in the world through his contacts in the aircraft and oil industries, he managed instead to instill in me his own estranged love of country life. However, six weeks working for a greedy farmer in North Wales, in winter, knocked that out of me too, and I came back to a comfortable job near home.

It would have been comfortable but for night classes. Going to catch the bus to them was like the walk to the condemned cell. I slumped in the seat, staring in blank misery at the rain-streaked

* Scots for 'marble'.

windows, hoping to miss the stop in the dark and that the bus would go on into the night for ever.

Dropping out of university at twenty-two, I reckoned I was too old to run home with my tail between my legs. Part of the university course was a field trials job at Chipping Ongar in Essex. I took it to fill the void.

My first sight of the Essex countryside had been in February, when I was interviewed. My impression was of low hills in the raw umber tones of wet, ploughed earth, and elm copses drawn in charcoal against a grey sky. Even in April the brightest colour among the opening buds on the copses was the incongruous Tube, writhing like a red rattlesnake through the fields. For some reason it went all the way to Ongar.

Despite a fondness for hills much higher than those found in East Anglia, I looked forward to my stay. The field trials work was outdoors and meant plenty of travel. I found lodgings in High Ongar, and my little room looked across the Roding Valley towards Chipping Ongar. In May the path to the tiny footbridge spanning the River Roding was heavy with the scent of hawthorn blossom in the overgrown hedgerows. Here, for the first time, I discovered some measure of contentment.

A warm summer and autumn were passed in the fields and lanes of Essex and Suffolk and the orchards of Kent and Herefordshire. I saw the huge sky of the fens grow dark at midday, filled with wind-blown peat like an Oklahoma dust-bowl storm, and acres of daffodils and tulips worthy of a Dutch landscape. One night, as we drove home in the dark, the bottoms of the clouds glowed ominously through a pall of smoke from an inferno of thousands of acres of blazing stubble. As far as the eye could see, flames carpeted the land as though the whole of East Anglia had been sacked and left to burn.

Despite good company, travel and work, I was marking time. Part of my life seemed destined to remain dormant. Somewhere, just out of reach, I knew there was a ready-made life that would fit me to perfection. Instead of reading about what other people were doing, I would either have something worth telling or be too taken up with my own affairs to bother.

One night, after walking my landlady's dog by the river, I was reading in front of the television. A programme called *Rivers of*

Pearl caught my interest, and I laid my book aside for a while.

The film concerned a man called Bill Abernethy. He made a living fishing for freshwater pearls in the rivers of Scotland and claimed to be the only full-time, professional pearl-fisher in Britain, having that occupation marked in his passport.

In a state of mounting excitement, I devoured every word, trying to find out how, and where, the pearls were found. He was shown selling two or three weeks' pearls to a Perth jeweller for over £200, but though he'd made more in three weeks than I got in three months, I paid little attention to financial matters. What struck me was that this man's living depended on nobody else. He took, at his leisure, what was there for the taking, submitting only to the dictates of weather and season. He went wherever the search for pearls took him, to places most of us enter only as tourists, searching in vain for roots that probably bind us to suburbia.

Torn from the limp complacency to which I was becoming accustomed, I was flung into a state of precarious indecision. I'd laboured under the illusion that the intense emotion that fed music and painting, and the vagrant spirit that had often set me adrift, alone even among friends, was dead and buried. Having lived so long in fear that dullness was synonymous with maturity, the resurrection of these feelings confused me.

It didn't take long to come to a decision, even though decisiveness was out of character. My landlady dozed on in her chair while I was in this turmoil, but the other lodger's newspaper rustled as if the wind of change had blown into the room. I told my employers right away, but decided to stay till early spring if they didn't mind. It was too late in the year to go off half-cocked looking for something I knew nothing about. I had the winter and spring to find out all I could about the pearl mussel and pearl-fishing.

2. Theory

Throughout early spring, I wrote to various scientific societies and libraries for journals and papers relating to the pearl mussel, particularly its distribution. I also wrote to Bill Abernethy, the pearl-fisher featured in the television programme I'd seen. It was a long job. Library books on aquatic life, which were my starting point, had nice pictures of dark brown, flaky-looking shells about five inches long, and a few lines which said that they were found 'in fast-flowing rivers and streams' and that they 'sometimes contained pearls of commercial value'. The bibliographies of these books had to be followed up before anything of value began to emerge.

Margaritifera margaritifera, as the species is known in the most recent papers, is an interesting creature in several respects beside its pearls. Though it never grows to more than sixteen centimetres approximately (6½ inches), it can live for over a hundred years. (If this seems a bit of a tall story, have a look at the mollusc section of the *Guinness Book of Records*.) Pearl mussels live in neutral to acid water in fairly fast-flowing rivers and streams in the temperate zone of the northern hemisphere. The further south they occur, the higher in the hills they tend to be found. The water they live in must have a high oxygen content; therefore cold conditions are preferable. They can even survive in streams originating in melting glaciers. These waters are, almost by definition, low in the calcium carbonate needed to construct the shell, and it is surprising that the pearl mussel can abstract enough to build a thick, heavy shell. The slowness of this process might have some bearing on the longevity of the species.

The longevity of the pearl mussel as a species is of interest. In the estimated 350 million years since its inception in the rivers of

Upper Devonian Asia, it has spread round the world's northern hemisphere, yet undergone so little change on its journey that it is as easy for us to recognize it in Canada as in Britain or Germany.

While many species of freshwater mussels are hermaphrodites, the pearl mussel has separate sexes. The males produce clouds of sperm which have to be inhaled through the females' inhalant siphon during feeding. Most washes away down river and is lost. When the female pearl mussels are fertilized, they store their gravid eggs in their gills ready to release the larvae.

The Unionoida, the order to which the pearl mussel belongs, are characterized by a unique, parasitic larval stage. In July or August the tiny free-swimming larvae, or glochidia, are released from the brood pouches in the gills. In order to survive, they must be inhaled by a trout or a minnow and attach themselves to the gills of the fish. Complete infestation of the gills suffocates the fish, and though this is unlikely to occur in natural conditions, quite heavy infestation might occur where mussels are very dense. The glochidia remain in the gills for something more than a week and, when they mature, measure about a tenth of a millimetre across.

At this stage, a further barrier to their survival occurs. Upon their release, apart from the chance of being eaten, they must fall into the right kind of bed. If the water is fast, the river bed will probably be composed of gravel and stones which have a grinding action, and the tiny shells will be crushed. The ideal type of water and substrate for their development seemed, from the literature, to be smoothly flowing water at the head of rapids, with an optimum depth of between half and 1½ metres. Later experiences showed this to be at least partially correct.

In Europe, the brown trout is the main host for the parasitic phase of the life cycle, though the minnow has also been cited. Interestingly, recent research has shown that the European pearl mussel is unable to develop in the introduced American Rainbow Trout, yet this fish is one of several hosts of the American pearl mussels' larvae.

Until very recently, almost nothing was known of what happened to the newly released glochidia when they fell to the bottom. There was no record of any shells being found that were smaller than about one centimetre in length, for many years. I have found shells less than half that size by simply sifting with my fingers the fine sand of a densely populated mussel bed in the Spey. The tiny mussels came out trailing little stones and coarse grains of gravelly sand from a spider's web-like thread. This is obviously the means by which they secure themselves to the bottom and is reminiscent of the byssal thread of sea mussels, *Mytilus edulis*. At that time, nobody had observed this characteristic as far as I knew.

Until the last few years, the pearl mussel has been in a scientific backwater since the early years of the twentieth century. Most of the data I obtained in that first winter was at least thirty years old, and the authors tended to quote the same nineteenth-century sources, or each other.

Eventually some information on the distribution of *Margaritana margaritifera* arrived. I was about to send it back when I realized that the paper was so old that it gave Linnaeus's original classification of the species. It was very vague. The British distribution was listed by counties, and vice-counties, whatever they were. The only way to extract the name of a river from this complicated system was when a county was listed, even though it did not actually have any pearl mussels in it. This meant that its boundary with the next county was the river containing mussels. If this doesn't seem well explained, it's because I still don't understand it myself.

Finally, a paper arrived with information of a general nature, and a list of rivers where the pearl mussel had been found, arranged in an alphabetical list of counties covering the British Isles. I still didn't see what was wrong with a map, but with the rivers named and the locations sometimes given to the nearest bridge or village, it could have been written for a pearl-fisher.

The accumulation of data I possessed was divided into distribution of pearl mussels and their biology. Anything mentioning pearls was in the category of ancient history or legend. The practice of the craft was not mentioned, yet pearl-fishing seems to have been an established industry (though I can't think of anything further from the modern meaning of that word) in Bronze Age Britain. Pearls found in grave goods of that period indicate that they were valued possessions and probably items of trade. Trade between Britain and the Roman Empire included wheat, hunting dogs and freshwater pearls.

The earliest written record of British pearls is to be found among the Roman writings of the first and second centuries AD. In his *Lives of the Caesars*, the Roman historian Suetonius says: 'Freshwater pearls seem to have been the lure that prompted his [Julius Caesar's] invasion of Britain: he would weigh them in the palm of his hand to judge their value ...'

It has been suggested that this often-quoted account is the result of pearls being substituted for pebbles of Cornish stream tin, another valuable British export of ancient times. Certainly the ore content of stream tin could be guessed by hand, but even large pearls are relatively light and are more accurately judged by eye. Size, shape, colour and lustre are the characteristics by which they are valued.

To illustrate this point further, the largest river pearl I have seen taken measured over a centimetre across yet weighed only $1\frac{3}{4}$ grammes, or one sixteenth of an ounce. Despite these attributes, its being the colour of a stale Malteser made it worthless.

Whether tin or pearls was the attraction, I don't know, but two other accounts from Roman times mention pearls in connection with Julius Caesar. Pliny's *Natural History* confirms that on Caesar's return from Britain he dedicated a breastplate covered in British pearls to Venus Genetrix and hung it in her temple in Rome. Contemporary Roman satirists saw it differently. In their view, Caesar had raided Britain to obtain pearls for his mistresses. This does not add much to the argument in favour of pearls being the lure, but it does tell us a lot about what Caesar's critics thought of him!

The second raid, in 54 BC, penetrated only a few miles north of the Thames, over a hundred miles from the nearest rivers containing pearl mussels, which tend to lie north and west of the Tees-Exe line. This, and the constant harrying by the Britons, ruled out any systematic search for pearls. Caesar's fondness for British pearls was probably more than satisfied by booty and tribute.

I have found no reference to Roman exploitation of British pearl fisheries after the Claudian invasion of AD 43, though an interesting coincidence intrigues me. The most northerly series of camps and signal stations, and the only legionary station in Scotland, lie just north of the rivers Isla, Tay, Earn, Allan and

Teith. All these are pearl rivers; the Tay, the largest and most famous, and the Isla and the Teith renowned for pearls of the highest quality. Just what was Agricola doing there in AD 84?

In pre-Roman Britain, before glass was available, pearl-fishing was even more of a hit-or-miss profession. Drawings of fishers, even as late as the Middle Ages, show them fishing 'blind'. They waded, almost naked, feeling for the mussels with their feet. On finding one, it would be raised either by ducking under to reach for it, if the water was deep, or by hand in the shallows. In ideal conditions of clear, shallow water, it is possible simply to walk along and pick the mussels out with the naked eye and gather them up. This would have been easy in ancient times when they would probably have been far more abundant in the shallows.

Some authors stated that the mussels were extricated from the river bed by means of a long, pointed stick being poked between the slightly open valves. The valves close on being touched and grip the stick tightly enough for the mussel to be dislodged from the bottom. The mechanics of the method work, but experience shows that this method is unlikely to have been useful to early fishers. The reason is that the mussel closes by reflex at the touch of the fisher's foot, or even the current of its approach. Pictures of pearlers in the Middle Ages, as I have already said, show that they did not use glass viewers. In the conditions of moving water, sun and wind, it is almost impossible to place such an implement into the half-centimetre opening that the mussel shows when feeding. Even without a glass to break the surface ripples, a cleft pole to grip the shell gets round these objections.

Only scattered references to what was obviously a valuable industry occur in medieval times. The pearl-fishery at Omagh, County Tyrone, is evidently of great antiquity, as it is reported that Gilbert, Bishop of Limerick, sent pearls from there to Anselm, Archbishop of Canterbury, in AD 1094.

In 1693 Sir Robert Redding sent pearls from the Omagh fishery to Dr Lister. He also wrote that there were four rivers in County Tyrone abounding in pearl mussels. Solomon Richards, in his description of County Wexford about 1656, speaks of the Slaney River as preceding all the Irish rivers for its pearl-fishing.

In Wales, the Conway was the most famous river. Other rivers there had pearl mussels and must have been fished, yet only the

Former distribution of pearl mussels in Britain

- Areas in which pearl mussels were formerly found
- Rivers or districts where they are extinct
- Regions which have never been colonized by pearl mussels, and unsuitable habitats
- No information at present

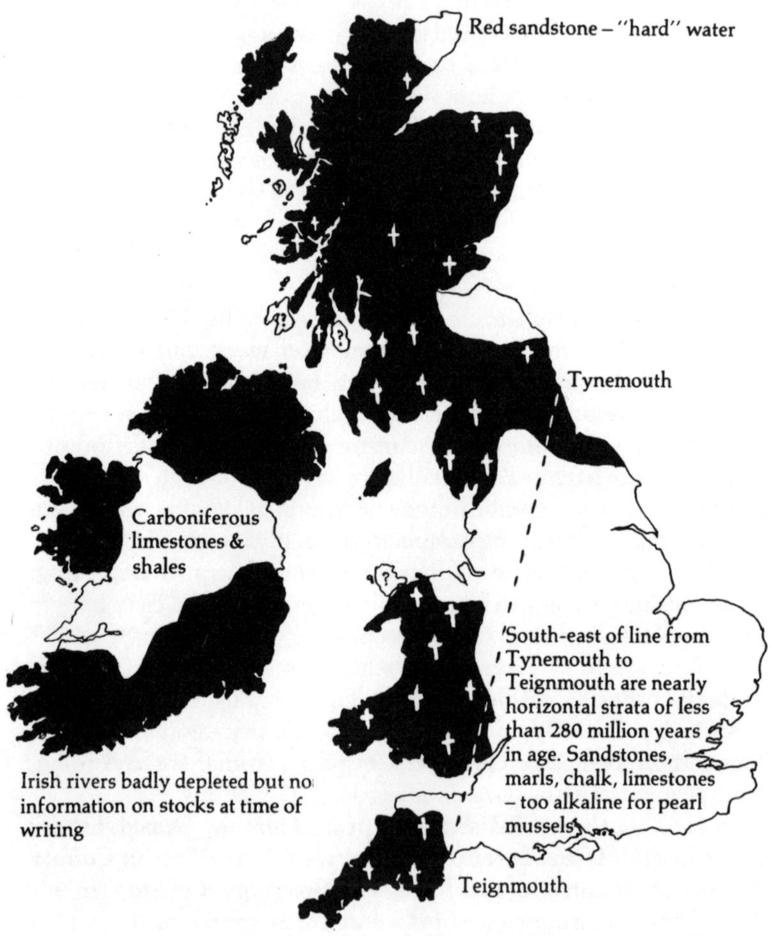

Conway and its little neighbour the now extinct Ogwen are mentioned in literature. There is a similar dearth of information about pearls in England. Only the Irt in Cumberland has any historical and literary connection with its pearls, yet rivers in Northumberland and Durham, several other Lake District rivers and a good few in Devon and Cornwall produced pearls. The Clun in Shropshire is mentioned in *Pearls and Pearling Life* by E.W. Streeter, published in 1886, probably as a result of a chance discovery during a period when pearl prices rocketed.

A few of the books about the Lake District and Snowdonia mentioned the Irt and Conway as once being famed for their pearls, and treasure-hunters pick up references in their magazine. This results in misguided optimists, with no knowledge of the craft, finding some of the last few mussels which might have stood some chance of breeding and, thinking this was their normal density, killing them.

The importance of Scottish pearl-fishing in ancient times is demonstrated by the fact that it is mentioned in a statute of the goldsmiths of Paris in 1355. This may not seem much to base its importance on, but Scottish pearls would then be competing with a similar product from several other fisheries situated within neighbouring Germany, and in France itself.

The Tay was, and still is, the most famous of the Scottish pearl rivers. It begins at the western end of Loch Tay where the rivers Dochart and Lochay meet below Killin, then enters Loch Tay, which is a mile wide and fifteen miles long. It is joined by the Lyon between Loch Tay and Aberfeldy, then enters the flood plain of Strathtay, where it is joined by its largest tributary, the Tummel. Above Dunkeld, the hills on either side close in again, and instead of turning east through Strathmore, which seems to be made for such a large river, it leaves that valley to the smaller Isla and cuts a narrow path south-eastwards towards Perth and the Firth of Tay beyond. About ten miles above Perth it is met by the Isla, and in the tidal reach below the city by the Earn. Its 120-mile length make it little over half the length of the Thames, though if the Tummel was taken into account, it would come closer. The entire system does not drain as large an area as the Thames, Severn-Wye or Trent-Humber, but its catchment area covers most of Perthshire and portions of Angus, Argyll and a corner of Inverness-shire. So much rain falls on the mountains of this large area that the Tay delivers the largest volume of water per hour of any river in Britain.

All the main tributaries that I have mentioned were once pearl rivers in their own right, and Perth became the centre of what must have been a valuable industry. It is difficult to reconcile such a scarcity of written record with a profession that is so ancient and so peculiar. Even today, despite the media's obsession with the absurd, pearl-fishing has largely escaped its notice. What little has been reported was mostly silly or belonged to the realm of fantasy. Perhaps injecting the boredom of daily life with the large doses of the sensational has the unfortunate side-effect of masking what is of real interest.

Whatever the low level of public awareness, Perth has continued to be the centre of the declining pearl business, and to this day it is one of the few places where a man with a bottle of pearls can get a fair price.

Finally, the long-awaited reply from Bill Abernethy came. I'd hoped that I might meet him and learn some of the mysteries that surrounded his craft. However, he didn't give away anything that my own researches hadn't already revealed about where to start. He did tell me I'd need body-waders, a glass-bottomed bucket and a 'forked stick' for picking up the shells. He suggested trying parts of England that I knew were chalk areas, well away from the older, hard-rock areas where pearl mussels were found. At first I thought this was to trick me, but I recalled an old article which had reported pearls being found in the streams of north Buckinghamshire. We'd probably been reading the same thing!

The problem of unreliable data has been handed down to future scientists in this field. My main source of rivers was a booklet published in the 1920s, based partly on the observations of Victorian amateur naturalists. When Dr Kerney of Imperial College collated the recent British survey of non-marine mollusca as part of a co-operative European venture, some erroneous data was included. Some of the Victorian observers had confused the duck mussel with the pearl mussel, and the survey has perpetuated the error for at least another quarter of a century.

Like most people, I had been under the impression that pearls are caused by grains of sand irritating oysters, or mussels. Even before experience showed that the incidence of pearls varies dramatically from one place to another, it should have been fairly obvious that some rivers were a good deal more fertile than others. As mussels live in sand and are so restricted in habitat, pearls would occur just as frequently in all rivers. The *Encyclopaedia Britannica* provided no more about pearl-fishing methods but did have quite a lot about pearl formation.

Oysters, and presumably mussels, are prone to infection by small, burrowing parasites which are taken in during feeding. When these enter the mantle, which is the skin lining the inside of the shell, they become encysted. The mantle's function is to produce a mother-of-pearl lining for the shell, and a ring of new growth around the edge or margin. This ring increases the volume of the shell to accommodate the growth of the animal's body in its rigid home. The growth of a pearl corresponds to the growth rate of the animal it is developing in. A cultured pearl in a marine oyster grows rapidly in tropical waters, reaching commercial size in as little as three years. The pearl mussel is very slow growing in its cold river, virtually devoid of the shell and pearl-making calcium carbonate; it can take five times as long to be useful to a jeweller, and may go on growing slowly for decades.

The beautiful lustre of pearls and the iridescence of nacre, or mother-of-pearl, are puzzling when one realizes that they are made of the same substance as limestone, eggshell and the chalk of the downlands. The more mundane forms of calcium carbonate are amorphous – that is, non-crystalline, or randomly arranged, particles.

Mother of pearl (nacre) and pearls are of two distinct crystal structures. The former has its crystals arranged almost parallel to the surface in a pattern of overlapping plates. This pattern interferes with light reflected from it, reflecting certain wavelengths more than others, depending on the closeness of the pattern. A coloured sheen or iridescence results. The vanes of feathers often show dark blue or green iridescence, and greenish or red sheen can even be seen in the fibres of thinly sliced boiled ham!

An American button-manufacturer looking for a substitute for mother-of-pearl from river mussels attempted to imitate the phenomenon by pressing the pattern onto steel buttons. He could have cornered the market if they hadn't rusted when the garments were washed.

Pearls differ from nacre by having their crystals arranged end on, possibly because they are situated in the mantle rather than below it, and receive new material from all sides.

Apart from its pearls, the pearl mussel itself seems to have been of negligible economic importance. The Manx, and possibly the Scots, used the valves as porridge scoops in ancient times. The Manx also made ornamental purses from the valves. When the black periostracal layer and the horny layer beneath are rubbed off, and the exposed nacre is polished, a multi-coloured rainbow like iridescence shines through. These purses were apparently quite popular in Victorian times.

In Europe, pearl mussels were used to fatten geese and were fed to pigs. There is little evidence of this type of exploitation in Britain, though they were used as bait by line fishers in the north-east of Scotland. The cod and ling-fishers of Peterhead and Aberdeen used to fill small boats with mussels from the rivers Ythan and Ugie in Aberdeenshire for this purpose, though presumably pearls were a welcome by-product.

3. Practice

So much data might give me a head start on some of the others who were bound to emulate the success of the pearl-fisher in the television programme, so perhaps college and university had not been a complete waste of time. I'd just enough money to hitch-hike to the rivers of South Devon, the nearest to Surrey that might produce pearls. A college friend, George Shand, and I had camped at his uncle's chicken farm near Totnes the previous year, and several rivers could be reached from there on foot.

It seemed so easy. I made a crude bottom-viewer from a one-gallon polythene bottle, cutting off the top and replacing the bottom with a piece of perspex sealed with a mess of black 'Bostick'. Fishing-tackle shops didn't stock body-waders, but I was sure they could be obtained in a fishing town like Brixham.

Saturday 22 April, 1971 was a good day to start a new life, but an unearthly silence and a strange light made me look out before dressing. Six inches of snow had fallen in the night. Though hot sun melted it by afternoon, I postponed my start till Sunday. There was no rush now.

At sunset the next evening I arrived at the chicken farm at Rattery. (In the light of later pearling experiences, the name was something of a coincidence.) I was invited to use the place as a base for the duration of my stay, fed and given a camp site.

In the morning I went into Brixham on the bus. Thinking that the Fisherman's Co-operative in the harbour would be bound to have body-waders, I was disappointed to have to part with £5 for mere thigh-waders, which would limit my search to shallow water. I packed my rucksack that night and prepared myself for a long, hard day, poring over the map in the light from the hurricane lamp.

The following morning saw me walking through the lanes with a rucksack containing waders, viewing glass, some rye bread, butter, a jar of honey, and a pipe and tobacco. The banks along the lanes were steep and high, their rocky sides cloaked in mosses and ferns, with wild violets sharing the damp shade with them. In sun-splashed shadow and on the open banks, clumps of red campion stood among masses of primroses. Cuckoos called from the copse, and the chatter of unseen brooks sounded in every dip in the road. Drinking deeply of each sight and sound, I spared a thought for George, sitting in the heavy silence of the university library, looking out on the grey rooftops and decaying brickwork of Liverpool's Myrtle Street.

I wandered on, avoiding main roads, eager yet unhurried, and revelling in my freedom like a newly released prisoner. Though not really expecting to find pearls on the first day, I was uncharacteristically optimistic and stopped to look in a couple of small streams on the way to the River Dart. Finding nothing in them, I walked on to Buckfastleigh, a lovely old town with a large abbey by the river, and the deep wooded valley where my real business was to begin.

The valley side was reached through a series of abruptly rising lanes at the back of the town. As I walked down a steep path under lichen-encrusted trees, the roar of water grew to a crescendo. Reaching the bottom, I pulled the waders on hurriedly and jumped into a shallow backwash where the river divided. The main volume of water roared down a rapid on the far side of a small island. After nearly an hour, bent double over my glass, with my stomach knotted with hunger and excitement, I was about to stop to eat. Two large black shells stared up at me from a patch of sand. In spite of my early optimism, I couldn't believe my eyes. Before picking them up, I looked away so as to repeat the moment of finding them, and to fix their position in my memory. They were half buried in the sand and, without a glass, were invisible among the ripples and small black stones. I was surprised to find them in such shallow water. The optimum depth was supposed to be between eighteen inches and 4½ feet, and these were in six inches of water.

I pulled them out of the sand and took them to the bank to examine their external features before opening them to look for pearls. They were about four inches long, covered with a black, flaky skin and very tightly closed. The thick shell splintered when I tried to lever it with a knife, and bent my thumbnails back as I attempted to pull the valves apart. I finally cut the hinge muscles with the knife and groped round the cold, wet animal for pearls. I'd no idea where to look for them, so pulped the whole body in my fingers. I saw the two powerful adductor muscles that held the valves closed, and was surprised to find they were little more than a quarter of an inch in diameter.

The pulped meat fell from the shell, revealing a beautiful iridescent mother-of-pearl lining. It was a silvery blue, shot through with salmon pink and green, and contrasted vividly with the dull exterior with its growth ring marks.

Upstream was a deep pool to be explored after I'd eaten. Quite a few shells protruded from the silt-covered sand of its bottom. They were mostly out of reach of my outstretched hand, and the thigh-waders began to fill in my efforts to reach them. It was a long walk back, but even without pearls, a couple of dozen shells on the first day made it certain that success was just around the corner.

Buoyed up by this, I spent the next ten days walking the course of another three or four rivers, but found nothing. However, the 'business' of pearl-fishing is a pleasure in any circumstances to me. Here, it was so inextricably entwined with the hills and streams, the forested valleys on the edge of the high moor, and the wild flowers and birdsong of the lanes, that I suffered no disappointment.

Only by returning to within a short distance of my first success did I find more mussels, about half a dozen much larger specimens and forty or so uniformly sized small ones, similar to those found on the first day. Further upstream was too rocky and fast for mussels, while downstream was ideal and equally devoid of them. Though I was very unsure of what this meant, it seemed that someone had fished out the lower river, leaving a few older shells at the upper limit of their range, and tiny, immature mussels that had grown in the intervening years. The entire river from Buckfastleigh to the tide at Totnes must have been full of mussels once.

Three weeks of perfect weather brought no pearls, so I went home. After my leisurely enjoyment of the steep lanes garlanded with wild flowers, a five-mile walk round the busy Honiton bypass with a seventy-pound pack rammed home the need for a car.

Odd jobs during the rest of the summer didn't pay enough for a car. When my only remaining school friend suggested a trip to Wales, I jumped at it.

We entered Wales via Wenlock Edge and Apedale. The little Standard Eight struggled over Long Myndd onto the moorland plateau and dropped gratefully down into Wales. I looked in the Wye, the Teifi and the Conway and found nothing, yet two years later, in the company of professional fishers, I was to see at least one mussel taken from each of these rivers. Tickets for an afternoon performance at the Royal Shakespeare Theatre dragged us away before I'd had time to try the Dee, and it was to be two years before the chance came again.

I bought a tiny old Austin on my return and immediately set off for Devon with some college friends, one of whom had a big dinghy. With the dinghy, I lifted all the shells in the deep pool on the Dart. They were so few and so small that I replaced them without opening them. I hope they are sufficient to enable them to breed and that they have been left in peace.

The following spring I went to the Lake District on what was meant to be the final attempt to find pearls in England or Wales. My battered journal was still my guide, my touching faith in it still undiminished. I won't give the name of this precious guide since it contains the names of one or two rivers which still have a chance of survival if left undisturbed.

The weather was cool and pleasant till I reached Coniston Water. Here a dank gloom enveloped the car, and my first glimpse of the mountains came through a pall of misty drizzle. Inexperience, ignorance, excitement and a new pair of body-waders made me immune to swollen rivers. I kept on to Newby Bridge. Mussels had been found near where Windermere emptied into the River Leven.

I hauled on my waders in fevered anticipation, cursing tangled straps and other minor hindrances. There seemed so much to do before I could get into the water. All this time the gigantic roaring wall of water, that I would normally have marvelled at, poured over the weir near the bridge. Eagerly scanning the river bed, I pushed out to waist depth. Why was I still walking on grass? The powerful current hit the baggy waders, and all I could do was run before it, stick flailing uselessly and pirouetting towards a deep pool. Still hanging on to my stick and glass, I came to a halt in the overhanging branches of a tree. It was a temporary haven. I couldn't let go of the branches to make for the bank. With courage born of ignorance, I headed downstream towards the bank, with my back to the current. Pushed out of control, and without knowing how, I reached the shallows, soaked, frozen and shaken.

Looking at the weir, it seemed so obvious. The river was in full spate, and only a fool would have tried to fish it, especially on his own. It had been a dangerous waste of time, but a valuable lesson.

Torrential showers continued the rest of the day and most of the night, so I slept in the car. Fortunately I had changed to a big Austin Cambridge which was only about eighteen inches too narrow for my length.

In the morning I started towards an apocalyptic gloom at Wrynose Pass. So much rain had fallen that the streams could no longer hold it. Water ran in silver-grey sheets down the slopes beneath the crags. The hills, robbed of any splendour, huddled miserably under their sodden blanket of cloud. At the top of Hardnott Pass shone a strange light. Looking down Eskdale, westwards, the sea burned gold beneath the clouds. The evening sun would soon creep beneath the edge of the clouds, bringing hope for the morning.

After my second raw, damp night in the car, I unfolded my cramped legs and drove to Santon Bridge on the River Irt, which, from the literature of the Lake District, seemed to have been a well-known pearl-fishery. The rain-swollen river was still small enough here to fish safely and produced a dozen shells in about three hours, not enough to make it pay. The sun beamed down on me as I took off my waders beside an old church above the river. I hadn't sufficient money to wait till the water fell, and there was no guarantee it wouldn't rain again.

On my way south I crossed the lower reach of the Irt, where my friends and I were later to find plenty of shells, and some beautiful pearls, on raids from north of the border.

This failure would have put a prospecting trip to Scotland out of reach, but a Danish family I did odd jobs for asked me to take their car up to Forres on the Moray coast, where they were going on holiday. With fuel paid, board with them for a week, and the use of the car when they came home, it was on.

On a perfect Sunday in mid-August, I left in great excitement, hoping to get there in one day. Just before dusk, I came over the hill on the outskirts of Perth and looked down on the great Tay winding through the city beneath the encircling hills. It was so big a river, I didn't see it ever being fished out. Not realizing that no filling stations were open in the 110 miles between Perth and Inverness on Sunday nights, I had to stop at Dalwhinnie at midnight and go on in the morning to the farm where the Kiertzners were staying.

One afternoon, with the car at my disposal, I went to Cromdale, the nearest point on the Spey. At last, this was it. There were so many shells I was at a loss; it was almost impossible to walk without treading on mussels, and they were all so big.

I had a cleft stick with me and tried to get some up to examine. Just as they were about to break the surface, they fell from the feeble grip of the stick. Why is it that at the moment you see your long-cherished goal, like a bad dream, something goes wrong? The sole of your shoe comes adrift, the car runs out of fuel or the phone rings. The split in the stick grew longer and its grip weaker. The shells I did manage to lift had to go in a pocket at the top of the waders. The waders then sagged and scooped water down my belly. I put some shells in the already scratched viewer. It held only three before its narrow field of view was obscured and the sand from the shells scratched it even more.

I was getting very frustrated when I spotted another pearl-fisher upstream on the other side and went up to see if it was Bill Abernethy, to whom I'd written.

The man's name was Williamson. I could hardly understand a word he said and didn't get much from him that would help me find pearls. He used a wooden, box-type viewer and found a brown pearl while I watched, which he just threw away. He told me that up near Grantown-on-Spey a band of about ten fishers were operating, some wading, others using a boat. At least there were plenty of others who might provide me with clues to my lack of success.

My last shells were opened in the kitchen of the farm. It was there that I saw my first pearl, if it deserves the name. It was about a centimetre long, part brown and part pink, shaped like a drip of fat that's congealed while running down the side of a pan.

So much for Scotland, I thought. My efforts to find a pearl, let alone make a living from them, were measured as a minus quantity. God forbid that I should have to go home with my tail between my legs and get a job in Camberley.

4. The Professionals

Finally I got the car for a whole day but wasted most of it mending a leaky jug and scouring the farm for a sack. Imagine a farm without a sack! About midday I left for Cromdale on the Spey with a polythene carrier bag and a still leaky jug. I was too excited to eat.

After twenty minutes in heavy water just below the bridge, at Cromdale, the bag was almost full. A young man in tweeds, holding a long salmon-rod, hailed me from the bank.

'I've clients fishing here this afternoon. You'll find plenty of shells down there under the trees. We can't fish there for overhanging branches.'

I walked downstream and opened my shells under the trees. A painstaking search produced nothing. With more shells than I'd ever had before, I wondered what had to be done to get pearls. Either they were very rare or there was something fundamental I'd missed.

The corner under the trees was deeper, but calmer. Large groups of big black shells clustered between black rocks. The stick didn't wobble so much in the slacker water and, despite being deeper, it was easier to keep my feet. However, the stick didn't grip the shells well enough to free them from the bottom, and always let them fall when I was just about to get hold of them. The viewer was dry and opaque and was very difficult to hold in the same hand as the bag of shells. After struggling like this for an hour or so, there was another shout from the bank. A portly figure, topped by a white stetson, looked down at me.

'Are you getting any?'

The accent had an American sound mixed with something else.

'A few,' I replied, thinking he meant shells. I was expecting to be moved on again when I noticed he had a pearling stick and a small, glass-bottomed bucket.

'God! What chance have I got if American tourists are pearl-fishing?' I mused as he came down to the water.

He wore no waders, yet waded straight out towards me. The white stetson shaded a round, tanned face, and a dark, pencil-thin moustache completed the Mexican caricature.

'Do you fish for a living?' I asked as he came alongside.

'No, but I used to before I went to Canada,' he replied in a strange mixture of Scots and American. 'I'm visiting my folk in Blairgowrie. My nephews fish for a living. A day at the shells is good fun, so I go with them.'

'You were born here, then?' I had to pin down his accent.

'Aye, but I've been sixteen years in Canada. I went wi' eleven of a family, and my wife died not long after.' He held out his hand. 'I'm Andra Stewart.'

We shook hands, then fished and talked till another shout echoed along the bank. Two men in green rubber body-waders, with sticks and buckets similar to Andra's, trotted down the steep bank into the trees and kindled a fire, then called us to the bank. Both men looked about thirty-five, though even close up it was hard to tell. The taller one had curly red sideburns peeping from under a red baseball cap that contrasted with his deep-blue eyes and green waders. He took off his cap to reveal a completely bald head, and fired a series of what I took to be questions at me. I looked blank. He spoke more slowly, but I still only got the odd word. His words poured out in a fierce tirade, yet didn't sound aggressive. Shrugging, he turned to his partner for assistance. He was a powerfully built man with regular features and unruly grey hair. In slower, plainer speech, he introduced himself as Neil McCormick. His partner was his brother-in-law, Donald McGregor, and Andra was Donald's uncle Andrew.

Meanwhile, Donald had been examining my stick and viewer with some amusement.

'Ged![1] Deek[2] the upside doon tangs!' He prodded the bag of shells. 'An' a polythene poke for a bag. Neily, deek the wild jug,[3]

[1] Travellers' word for brother, comrade etc., used as general exclamation.
[2] 'Look' or 'See' in travellers' dialect.
[3] Bottom-viewer.

Tangs and jugs

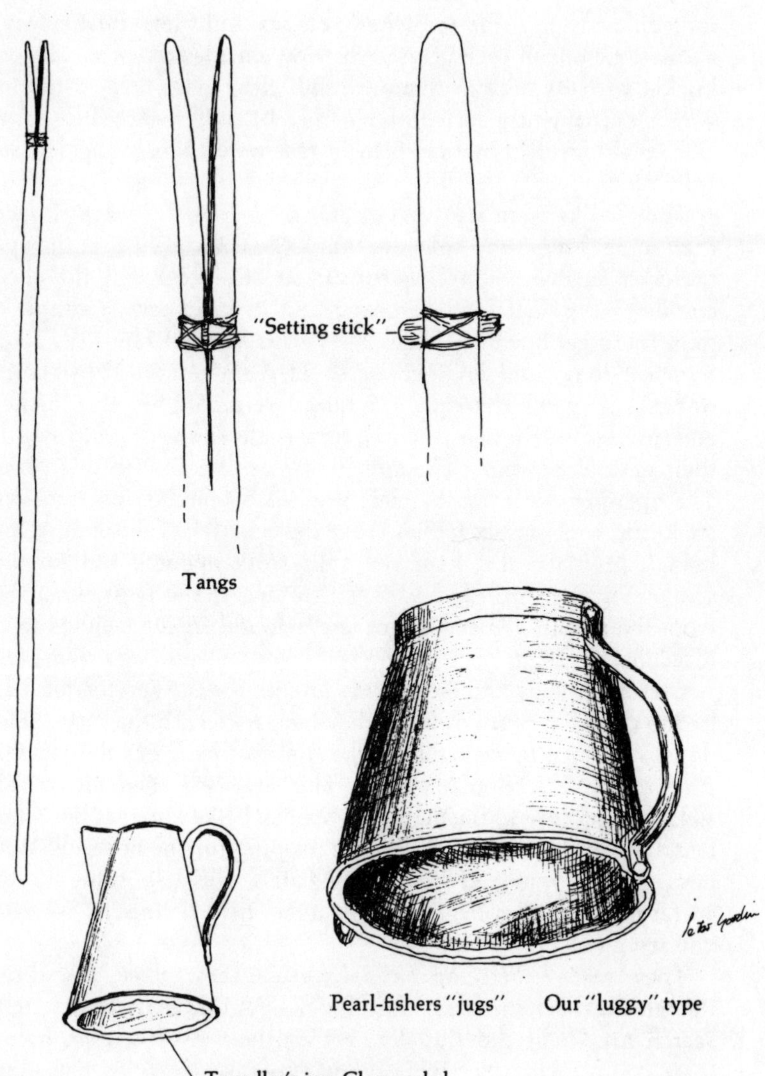

Pearl-fishers "jugs" Our "luggy" type

Traveller's jug. Glass sealed with candle grease (wax)

ged! The laddie cannae see a hait.'[1]

He passed the polythene viewer to Neil, who peered incredulously into the scratched perspex and black Bostik. They showed me one of their 'jugs', which was made from a small metal bucket with its bottom removed, and clear glass held in the top with a permanently soft putty. A metal handle was bolted to the side, enabling it to be held firm in fast water which buckled and split mine.

Their sticks were also very neatly made, and far more efficient than mine. I'd simply split the thin end of mine. In use, the split travelled further up, till there was so little grip that the shells couldn't be pulled from the sand and it could take a couple of minutes to get one in the bag. They used straight ash poles about five feet long, and an inch or so in diameter for their 'tangs' (tongs). To make the split, the tangs were held loosely, thickest and forward, as though reaching for a shell, and allowed to assume their natural position. The split was made vertical to this plane. The opening width of the cleft was set by binding an iced lolly stick into it about six inches from the 'mouth'. The binding that held it in place also kept the split from opening too far and weakening the grip of the tangs. Moving the lolly stick further from the mouth allowed larger shells found in some rivers to be lifted just as easily.

Even their bags had certain advantages for the specific job they had to do. They were ordinary hessian sacks with the tops folded down inside to make a half-sack. A strip torn from the top was used to make a shoulder strap. The strap was tied on the top slightly unevenly so the mouth of the bag bellied out a little. Shells could be put in without looking or groping for the opening. With hessian, the water drained immediately the bag came to the surface, when other bags (such as mine) held pounds of water as you struggled up the bank.

They opened their shells rapidly while they talked, and threw the remains back into the water. I took about three times as long to search my shells individually, yet finished my bag long before them. With their superior tools and expertise, they had picked up far more than I had. The tops of their upturned jugs were dotted

[1] 'Anything' in this usage. 'Nothing' in Old Scots.

A pearl-fisher's view of a good crook

Tanging a shell

with pearls waiting to go into the glass aspirin bottle that already had a dozen or more in it. I'd not even got a brown pearl, which they'd been throwing away.

'How do you do it?' I asked in amazement. 'I'm doing the same thing in the same place as you, and I've nothing.'

'Ye've got tae look for crooks,' Neil said, holding a shell out for me to see. I looked at it closely. It had a deformity. A deep groove ran from near the eroded portion by the hinge to the outer margin. The margin was buckled. He took it back, inserted one valve of a mussel into the bottom, cut the lower hinge muscle, twisted, and it opened up. A large brown pearl bulged in a sac in the skin that lined the inside of the shell. 'Nae use. It's pure broon, ged.' He tossed it into the bottom of the bag. Andy showed me another crook, this time with a pearl sitting deeper in it. He popped it out into his palm. It was lovely pink colour, and conical in shape.

'A nice wee button, Andra,' Donald commented.

I hung on to every word, just in case we didn't meet again, but when I mentioned English rivers, they were just as interested as I was in keeping in touch. Neil and I swapped addresses, and I said I'd call on the way south.

The ghillie who'd asked me to move never came back, and Donald and Neil fished up through the stretch I'd left, then we all gathered at the fire for a last 'opening'. By the time they'd gone through all their shells, there was over half an inch of pearls in the bottle. I still had nothing.

I looked at Andy, standing at the fire. 'How did you stand it with no waders? I'm cold as it is.'

'We never wear waders at the Tay,' Neil said. 'There's holes fifty feet deep in the Tay.'

'Aye, vicious dungeons,' chipped in Donald.

'If ye slip on the edge of a hole,' continued Neil, 'at least ye can swim back tae the shallows if ye've nae waders. It's nae use in the Tay wi' waders unless it's bone dry. The shallows are fished oot.'

I tried to imagine five or six hours' immersion to the neck in freezing water, rapids that could lift you off your feet and sweep you into 'holes' fifty feet deep, and a good chance of coming home empty handed. It sounded as though there was a fair risk of not coming home at all. I assumed it must be worth the risks.

'The Tay can be a dour burn,' Neil told me, 'but if ye get a pearl, it could be a big yin.'

They left before I did, as they'd over eighty miles to go, and I went back to the farm with a bag of mussels which I opened in the kitchen. To my surprise, a little pearl popped out of one shell before I'd seen it. It fell in the sink, but I rescued it. It was banana-shaped and a lustrous pink colour. Hannah Keirtzner claimed it, offering me whatever the jeweller said it was worth.

On my last try at the Spey I took George Linder from the farm with me. With thigh-waders and a jug with polythene stretched over the bottom, he had a hard time. It was cold and wet, but I got six nice pearls, together worth about £20. I was there only 2½ hours. In my last job it would have taken me a week and a half to earn that much.

A few days later, my Danish friends left, and I followed as far as Old Rattray to call on the pearl-fishers and to meet Martin Brooker, my companion on the futile Welsh trip.

Arriving a couple of hours before Martin, I took out the torn cigarette packet that Neil had written his address on and found Yeaman Street, a cul-de-sac near the Rattray Cross. I drove in slowly, and a striking-looking woman with an explosion of tightly curled, dark hair, with a 'Mallen Streak', (a characteristic of Catherine Cookson's fictitious Mallen family) looked up from picking up papers in the yard between two houses.

'Does Neil McCormick live here?'

She shouted at the door of the nearest house. 'Neily! There's someone here tae see you.'

Neil's grey head popped round the door in surprise. 'Come in mun, Come in!' He shouted across the yard: 'Donald! Look wha's here!' Donald's bald head bobbed through a broken window in the cottage opposite, then he came out, followed by his wife. They crammed behind us into a low-ceilinged room already overflowing with children lying on the floor in front of the television.

Introductions were not easy for me, a stranger in a foreign land who couldn't speak the language, enthusiastically welcomed amidst a babble of children's voices and a television on full volume. To add to the general difficulties, Neil was married to Donald's sister Mary, and Donald's wife was called Mary too.

It seemed only minutes had passed when I had to leave to meet Martin. We left his girlfriend in a bed-and-breakfast and sought a campsite, then all went to Neil's in the evening and stayed talking till the early hours in the packed room.

Next day we went sightseeing, then spent the evening at Donald's. There was the usual crowd there. Both families made eleven, there were the three of us, and, for a while, Andra and his two daughters. Andra and the girls had just left when a commotion started in the yard outside. Suddenly a big man burst into the room, red-faced and bellowing with rage. We three could only watch in open-mouthed, uncomprehending silence as the argument was tossed between the man and Donald like a battered tennis ball. Eventually, caught between the raging argument and the children sniggering and smirking in barely disguised amusement behind our chairs, we didn't know which way to look. It ended as abruptly as it began when the big man disappeared into the night. I could only hazard a guess that it all concerned a fishing rod, and was left with a strange sensation that the whole thing was part of a dream. We'd started the day in Britain but without noticing, had been transported to another country with a different language and customs.

The boisterous vitality was intoxicating and when I left that night, I knew I'd be back because it was where I belonged.

Martin wanted to try pearl-fishing before he went home, so I borrowed an extra jug, tangs and waders from Donald and Neil and gave him my gear. Neil suggested we try the South Esk, a small river in nearby Glen Clova. I was keen to see what difference the 'professional' equipment would make.

Immediately I put on the thin, seamless rubber waders I noticed their lightness and flexibility. Walking was little different from when wearing thicker trousers, but climbing fences, almost impossible in my seamed, canvas stretchless outfit, was so easy that an accident on barbed wire was far less likely.

The jug, made from a metal 'luggy', a small bucket for picking raspberries into, was also far superior. The glass seemed positively brilliant so that shells I would have missed with my contraption flaunted themselves in my view. The sloping sides of the bucket gave a far wider field of view so that peripheral vision picked up a lot that I would have passed by. When the water was quick, the rigid metal handle allowed the jug to be kept on target and moved rapidly to and fro in the zigzag pattern the fishers follow in the water. Mine would have buckled and burst if used in this manner. The jug I have now is the one I made the following year with the same materials, and it has had only two or three glasses in it in ten years' hard use.

Before cold legs forced Martin to give up, he found one small button pearl – that is, one of small, round, conical shape. I got one large pearl with a band round it so it looked like two different-sized spheres fused together.

I walked back to the car in the silent glen, trying to grasp the reality of being there, and not as a tourist, but with real purpose. It was still impossible to equate the place, and the pleasure of being there, with work. Camberley had virtually ceased to exist. The tunnel-vision of town living, blinkered by building and street, was now free to range from the tiny flowers at my feet to distant hills bathed in afternoon sunlight. It seemed fitting that the eye should reflect as much from within as it did from without.

This pleasant drift was quickly banished when a kamikaze motor-cyclist forced me off the road. He and his wife survived intact, the Kiertzners' car did not. My banjo, fiddle and guitar in the back were all right, fortunately. I phoned Otto Kiertzner and nearly sank to the ground in relief when he said, 'It's only tin. Are you OK?'

When Martin and I finally reached Yeaman Street that evening, the story was greeted almost with relish.

'Donald! He's smashed the man's car, ged!' Neil bellowed into Donald's door.

'NO! Have ye telt him yet?' Donald queried, gloating at the prospect.

Questions came from everywhere as we queued to get in the narrow doorway of Neil's house. Martin and his girl were leaving the next day so we'd brought some cans of beer and sat till late.

The pearl-fishers never seemed to have anything to do the next day that was more important than the enjoyment of talk and company, especially where it concerned pearls. Because they were never put out by unexpected company, the world beat a path to their door.

Next morning, Martin and I broke camp and went into Rattray. I saw him off. Without a car I would have to stay near to the town, and I wanted to fish with Neil and Donald for a while before going home. There was always raspberry picking if things got really low.

After Martin and Terri had gone, I walked up to Yeaman Street with my huge load. Their old blue Wolseley wasn't there, but the 'Two Marys' were at home, and they told me the men had gone to the Tay. Disappointed at missing an opportunity to fish the legendary Tay, I wondered what to do. It was impossible to wander round the town all day with an eighty-pound pack and four musical instruments, nor could they be left in the tent anywhere near the town. Fortunately the men came back early, and when I mentioned picking raspberries, they laughed.

'Picking berries is nae use tae anyone,' Donald told me in no uncertain terms. 'Ye'd be better off fishing wi' us.'

'Aye, the picking's just aboot finished anyway,' added Neil in obvious relief. They had a few acres which interrupted their pearl-fishing for a few weeks each summer.

'See if ye can find a bit o' grund at the bottom o' the gerden,' Donald suggested. 'Watch oot for scrap iron and barbed wire, though.'

Once the tent was up, I cooked and ate a bowl of porridge, only to be called from Neil's: 'Come in, man, and get some meat. There's nae need tae sit doon there in a void.'

My behaviour was obviously strange to them. Everyone else just walked in the door and made themselves at home, being offered whatever was cooking at the time, and there always seemed to be something on the stove.

One morning Donald called me in from the bottom of the garden. Andy Stewart and his daughter Brenda were being given breakfast, and I was asked to sit with them. Even assuming everyone was being fed, I was still flabbergasted at the huge bowl of eggs and mound of toast that Mary put on the table. When it became apparent that only Andy, Brenda and I were eating, it was obviously impossible. After half-a-dozen eggs and two or three slices of toast, I was sunk. Andy appeared genuinely concerned about my health. 'Eat up, laddie, there's plenty of eggs. Mary, the laddie's no weel'(well).

One morning we'd been hanging round the yard and two or three other men joined us. Nobody seemed to have a job to go to. We decided to go to the Tay, which meant fishing without waders. Leaving the road about five miles south of Blairgowrie, we went down a track towards the river. Not having waders, we just grabbed our jugs, tangs and bags and trotted down the steep bank towards the broad, fast-flowing waters. There was a hard day ahead for me, unaccustomed to the rigours of five or six hours' almost total immersion, spiced with Donald's tales of 'dungeons' and 'vicious streams', his terms for deep pools and rapids. With mixed dread and excitement, I hurried towards my initiation.

Fishing beside Neil and Donald, I could watch their actions, and they could keep an eye on me. Forcing against the current, with my leather moccasins slipping at every step, I was walking on the spot, while Donald and Neil forged ahead, lifting mussels on the move. Their bags were bulging with shells and could hardly be lifted when they came out of the water. The bottle of pearls mounted gradually, while I couldn't even get a brown one.

The initial plunge is not so bad, as the prospect of finding pearls takes the edge off it. However, after a couple of openings it is customary, and necessary, to light a huge fire of driftwood at which everyone gathers for 'a heat' and an opening. From a distance, this must appear a weird ritual in slow motion. Clothes steam as we strike grotesque postures round the fire, trying to dry inaccessible parts of our clothes and avoid the smoke. The posturing may be accompanied by spasmodic leaps and yells when someone overheats a tender part of the anatomy.

It is after drying out, and getting slightly warmer, that the prospect of going back really becomes a test of character. Each return to the water becomes more of an ordeal. Blood-curdling groans burst through clenched teeth as the water passes the genitalia and creeps up the belly. Although I became inured to the hardships to a similar degree to my friends, I believe the body never truly becomes accustomed to such treatment but no longer registers the damage inflicted on it. It is the same as prolonged heavy drinking. I have found myself putting my hands in the icy water to warm them and sheltering from a breeze by going into deeper water. Usually only our heads remained dry, and the smokers kept cigarettes in hats, or shoulder straps, and still got them wet.

Fishing on upriver and leaving the fire far behind, there was only one tiny respite from the increasing coldness. I've never forgotten the first time I tried it. Neil had just come out of the water and was standing on the rocks looking exceptionally pleased with himself. What I'd thought was river water draining was a stream of urine rushing from the bottom of his trouser leg. I was on my way to the bushes to relieve myself and thought it was worth a try. It was marvellous. All the years of pent-up guilt and shame melted away. The warmth and sheer freedom must make it rank as one of the greatest lost pleasures of childhood.

At the end of the day we walked back down river at a tremendous rate, despite the absence of a definite path, and a decided lack of feeling in the legs. Hauling up steep slopes, ducking under fallen trees, climbing over rocks or wading out round those too big to tackle, we returned to where we'd entered the water, without slackening our pace.

We flung our jugs and wet bags in the boot, our tangs down the side of the seats, and ourselves, soaking as we were, onto the seats in a tangle like sleeping piglets. Only the driver could move. Somehow the smell of mussels clung to the hair and clothes, a tang of fresh water with a faint echo of the sea in it. This was soon swamped by more powerful odours of steaming clothes, and the smoke of long-awaited cigarettes.

Five hours in a mountain river drain every last drop of thermal energy from the body and replace it with an indescribably voracious appetite. It certainly was an initiation.

The reason for going without waders in the Tay, and the confirmation of Donald's lurid tales, came when we fished just above the Campsie Linn, a small falls. Here the river runs east along a fault in the rock till it breaks out to the south down the low waterfall. Wading out from the north bank above the falls, the fisher finds that the water flows over a sheet of rock with pockets of sand in it where a few shells may be found. From waist depth the water shallows as the mid-point of the river is reached, until it drops to thigh depth in places. Here, two thirds of the way towards the fifteen-foot cliff that forms the opposite bank, a shadow can be seen. It appears to be cast by the cliff but, when seen through the jug, it turns out to be the other side of the fault, an underwater cliff, down whose vertical side it is possible to see into around twenty feet of water before a seeming infinity of inky blackness cuts off the view.

Donald and Neil told me that to fish these edges with waders was suicidal. Shells could be taken from the narrow, sand-filled ledges that occurred in the cliff face. This required the fisher to walk the brink, 'leaning' on the water, using the buoyancy of the jug for support, trying to spot black mussels in the semi-darkness beneath the overhang. If you lost your footing, without waders you could easily swim the few feet back to standing depth. Sometimes the ledges form a boundary between calm shallows and deep, fast water. Falling here, after several hours' immersion has robbed the legs of feeling, would have almost certainly been fatal.

Despite the greater experience of my friends, I didn't think that waders would drag me down. After all, the water inside would only weigh the same as that outside, not being any more dense, and dry clothes held a lot of air. We did agree on one point: you could reach a lot more shells without waders, and with the shallows of the Tay already depleted, that was crucial to finding pearls. Either way, danger came second.

The theory was put to the test about five years later. I was fishing on my own in Glen Clova in early April, when the snow was still on the hills. Climbing along a sloping edge of a pool about eight feet deep, I saw shells among the sand and weeds ahead, where the water began to become shallower. Reaching the shallows, where the water was about waist depth, I moved further from the bank to reach the shells which were just behind me. The current caught me off balance, and my feet couldn't get any grip on the sloping shingle. As I pitched slowly backwards into about eight feet of very cold water, I suddenly remembered a television programme in which the Lakeland author and naturalist Hugh Falkus threw himself into the River Esk in an anorak and thigh-waders to demonstrate that a fisherman could float in these conditions if he kept his arms down and didn't panic. The part of the Esk Mr Falkus chose was faster-flowing than where my accident occurred. He just let the current take him down into quieter, deeper water. Here, an eddy took him to the side where he was able to reach some overhanging branches.

I calmly maintained an upright position in the water and found that I sank only to the armpits. Though my waders were filling, a tight belt slowed the rush down. Paddling gently forward, my feet soon touched bottom again, and I walked out. Taking my waders down to empty them, I found the water hadn't reached my feet. Hugh Falkus's demonstration had probably saved my life.

In many other parts of the Tay, and other rivers, there are shallows well away from the bank. If the fisher comes on one and finds shells on it, he naturally continues fishing upstream until it eventually runs into a deep pool. Here, you are forced to head for the side, only to discover that you have been wading up a long bank flanked by deep water. Retracing your steps with the current pushing you in the back is like running down a steep hill, and an optical illusion created by the jug makes the bottom appear to shelve away deeper, where logic tells you that you've already been able to wade safely.

If you neglect to make a mental note of a prominent tree or rock where you got out to the bank, it could mean half an hour's panic-stricken search for the only wadeable bridge between yourself and safety.

Neil once had to swim out of such a predicament, but only after throwing his jug and stick to shore and tying his bag of shells more tightly round him. Not wearing waders, and being a strong swimmer, his reluctance to ditch a bag with some good crooks in it did not cost what it might if I had done the same.

Davy Bell, who did not like swimming in places where he could not touch the bottom now and then, got into the same position once. He threw his bag and tangs to the bank but kept hold of his jug. If his jug had been dropped, that would have been the end of his day's fishing. Between his precarious position and the bank was a deep, fast-flowing piece of water that flowed into an even deeper pool. As Davy headed towards the side, he lost his footing and was carried down into the pool, paralysed with fear but still clinging to his jug, which helped keep him afloat till Neil's outstretched tangs came into reach.

5. South of the Border

In a week of fishing the Tay, the soles of my shoes had worn through and I hadn't made enough to patch them, let alone buy new ones. Donald and Neil had accumulated quite a bottle of pearls and were keen to make an exploratory trip to the rivers south of the border that I'd told them about. Their nephew, 'Wee Andy' Stewart, and a neighbour, 'Big Davy' Bell, were going too. Word got round other weekend pearl-fishers, and several of them dropped in after 'The George' had shut with a 'kerry oot'.

A 'quiet evening' with the McCormicks and McGregors had turned into a party by the time another eight or ten people had jammed themselves into the little room where the two families and I already made twelve. We stood shoulder to shoulder, drinking and talking, peering at each other through the clouds of cigarette smoke that hung just below the ceiling. About one in the morning the others began to leave, hanging reluctantly at the door, envious, yet wishing us luck, and telling us how lucky we were just to be able to go as we pleased. As if I didn't know!

Despite being so late to bed, preparations began before 7.30 a.m. The old Wolseley was first loaded with tents, blankets and food. My instruments were put in as I was continuing homewards when the raiders returned to Scotland, then the remaining space was filled with jugs, bags and waders till the chance of our getting in seemed pretty remote. Excitement gripped everyone, not just those directly involved but the women and children as well. The yard between the houses buzzed with activity, and neighbours, sensing something was afoot, gathered to see what it was. It was evident that years of setting-off for new rivers had not dulled the anticipation that Donald and Neil felt.

It felt good to be on the road again. After an hour or so, the car became a cocoon in which we were suspended between the familiarity of home and family behind, already almost forgotten, and the uncertain future that lay over the horizon. The soothing drone of the engine was a comforting background to the comments on rivers we passed, and speculation on what those ahead might hold. This was our home, the road that led to the river. We passed through a world from which we seemed to need little, yet to which we belonged more closely than many of those we shared the road with.

Donald and Neil obviously had scant regard for anyone who had the misfortune not to be a pearl-fisher, or at the very least they pitied those who lacked some degree of self-reliance. Now, with the swaggering bravado of border reivers, the Scots were sweeping down to rob the English rivers of pearls, right under the noses of landowners who'd yet to learn that they could not prevent the plunder.

We were not the first 'Scotchmen' to try the rivers of the Lake District, it seems. In a collection of photographs taken in the Lakes between about 1860 and 1900, I saw pictures of travelling pedlars, called 'packmen' or 'Scotchmen', who travelled on foot carrying a bundle of wares and who were mostly Scots. The Scots travelling people still sell dishclothes, rugs etc. round the door, so it is highly likely that these packmen were tinker folk from the Galloway district just across the Solway Firth. If so, they would also be pearl fishers and would have found the rivers of Cumberland and Westmorland irresistible.

The following year, when I was living with Neil and Donald, an Indian door-to-door salesman called with a van full of clothing. Neil answered the door. 'Mary, it's the packy-man.' Mr Singh, not yet reconciled to British ignorance of Asian geography so soon after our relinquishing control of his country, explained emphatically: 'I not Paki man, I Indian man.' He was quite flattered to be thought of as a packman though.

We swooped down across the border near Carlisle and raided a chip shop in Cockermouth. As the sun gave way gradually to a pearly evening light, we reached Ouse Bridge, where the River Derwent leaves Bassenthwaite Lake. Excitedly we rummaged for jugs and waders, snatched the tangs from the roof rack and rushed down the bank. Despite our rapid deployment over several hundred yards of river, nobody found shells.

'Nae bottom,' Donald replied curtly to my puzzled look when we met at the car. Knowing nothing of 'bottoms', I got back in my seat.

We skirted the north shore of the lake till we reached a bridge over Chapel Beck, the next place in the journal.

'Mair like Chapel Beak,' snorted Donald, referring to beak-shaped mussels that were usually barren of pearls.

Everyone set off downstream towards the lake shore, then suddenly turned back before I'd caught up with them.

'What's wrong?' I asked as they began taking off their waders.

'It's nae use,' Neil sighed, 'they've dug oot the burn a' the way tae the loch.'

'Weren't there any shells in the stuff they dug out?'

'No, it was done years ago,' he grunted as he struggled with his waders. 'There's devil a hait left noo.'

The alteration of watercourses for various reasons has had a drastic effect on mussels. In this case, a small beck with only about half a mile of mussels had been made extinct as a result of a farmer's deepening and banking its course to prevent its flooding his fields. In other rivers, the shallow mussel beds have been dug out to make the place more attractive to salmon. In the only pearl stream of note in north-eastern France, fishers diverted the river in order to expose the mussels completely. Rather like cutting down your trees to reach the apples. It was sad to think that the mussels in Chapel Beck had probably taken several thousand years since the end of the last Ice Age to establish themselves so far up the Derwent system.

A sad, grey twilight had stolen quietly over the hills since we'd left the Derwent, so we called it a day.

Neil saw me looking at the map. 'Better see if ye can find a place tae put up the tent.'

In later years it would have been normal to have just got into the car and headed, or 'held on', as Neil said. We'd have passed several burns that we should have fished during the night, and most likely would have to go to the expense of a return trip to check them out.

'Aye, and near a pub,' added Davy Bell, as an afterthought.

In Bassenthwaite village, which Donald called 'Bathenswaite', till nobody was sure which it was, we found an inn. Beyond the village we pitched the tent on a grassy strip beside Chapel Beck and cooked the typically greasy mess favoured for speed of preparation, devoured it and made for the inn to pour alcohol on top of it. The friendly little inn was full of shepherds, farmers and heavy-booted, woollen-stockinged hill-walkers.

'Och, we'll try the local brew,' Donald volunteered. 'Mak' it half pints in case we dinnae like it.'

'Ye can tell it's his roond,' muttered Big Davy.

'Ged! That's wild beer,' spluttered Neil, reverting to a mixture of broad Scots and traveller's 'Cant' to avoid insulting any sensitive locals.

It was terrible. We forced it down and looked for something more tolerable.

'Better wi' nips,' was Neil's patriotic inspiration. He ordered five whiskies. Donald pulled his sleeve urgently. 'They've got Wee Heavies, Neily,' he cried, pointing to bottles of strong Bass on the shelf, including them in Neil's round. Nips and 'Wee Heavies' went on till closing time, and the car got us to the tent despite random interference from the man in the driver's seat, whoever it was.

Beneath the trees, in the misty grey dawn, we stood round a large fire demolishing a heap of bacon, eggs and baked beans. Having slept through the roar of the beck, I wondered at feeling hunger instead of nausea.

We crammed the gear in the car. There was no point in careful packing when the boot and interior were both already a mess of pastry crumbs, cigarette packets, abandoned socks, chip papers and empty cans and bottles. Neil had been using the dashboard top as an ashtray since we left Blairgowrie. The smell of all this, and us, was blended with the all-pervading smell of petrol.

We looked at the next three rivers from bridges. I was too tired and too inexperienced to press for a more thorough search. The great mystery factor, 'the bottom', was not right. I evidently had a great deal to learn concerning 'bottoms'.

At the Leven, which was much lower than when I had nearly lost my life in it, we found no sign of the remaining shells that were supposed to be near the lake's outfall. The Rothy, at the north end of the Windermere, which I had managed to fish, was summarily dismissed, and only the Irt remained.

My research had produced plenty of information about pearl mussels but virtually nothing about pearl-fishing, or the incidence of pearls. The most celebrated English pearl river was undoubtedly our next target, the Irt. Though it is only a small river, the quality of its pearls was of the highest order. Camden, in his great work *Britannia*, mentions it and records the peculiar belief prevalent in ancient times regarding the formation of pearls: 'The shellfish having by a kind of irregular motion taken in the dew, which they are extremely fond of, are impregnated and produced pearls.' This widespread notion was fully explained in pseudo-scientific writings of the time, even including drawings of the mussels surfacing at night to imbibe the dew.

In Elizabethan times, the only way to protect a fishery was to take out a patent on it, and it was by this means that the circumnavigator Sir John Hawkins controlled the Irt. Since the time of Charles II a Royal Charter has allowed fishers access to any river in order to seek pearls, though the reception we receive in some places would indicate a prohibition order against us.

Although my companions had travelled most of the highlands of their own country, the steepness of Wrynose and Hardnott Passes and the aggressive upthrust of the surrounding hills drew gasps of surprise from them. Leaving the high country, we cut through the beautiful wooded foothills between Eskdale and the Irt to Santon Bridge, where I'd found shells on my rain-sodden expedition. We found a few shells, but again it was the bottom that put Donald and Neil off. 'Doon the way' would be better, so we went to Holmrook, where the main road crossed the river which was much slower running here.

We parked in a lay-by at the bridge. Donald looked at me expectantly. 'You've got the easy waders,' he said by way of excuse. 'Easy waders' were far from easy. Though they had an integral boot which saved a few seconds in putting them on, their rigid, seamed construction made raising the leg to climb a fence a major effort.

Scrambling down the bank, I climbed arthritically over a barbed-wire fence and entered the water just below the bridge. It barely reached my knees and was crystal clear. Two massive, jet-black shells appeared almost as soon as my jug touched the surface. I lifted one, and the others let out a roar as I held it up towards them where they lounged indifferently on the wall above me. They'd begun to doubt the word of the journal and obviously didn't expect such quick results.

'Never been fished for four hundred years!' Donald shouted as he bagged his first shell within seconds of entering the water. 'There's been naebody at this burn since that rectumnavigator what's 'is-name.' I'd told Neil and him about Sir John Hawkins' patent.

Contrary to the usual practice of fishing upstream, we went down-river towards the sea. It wasn't far to tidal water, taking less than two hours. On the way back we fished more slowly and took some massive, gnarled old crooks from the little meanders where the water came to the top of the waders. Some parts we had to skirt round, reaching into the semi-darkness for shells, or what might be shells, facing us side on. One man went round each side of the deep if it was possible, lifting shells at the full reach of the stick to try to overlap his partner's ground.

Neil and I got out to join Davy for an opening on a corner near an old packhorse bridge, when we realized we were being watched. A man and small boy were taking a keen interest in our activities. Donald, who was still in the water, automatically assumed that we were about to be threatened with expulsion by a water bailiff and tried to defuse the situation with breezy chit-chat.

'I bet ye havnae seen anyone daein' this before,' he said, trying in vain to moderate his broad Scots.

'You're looking for pearls aren't you?' the stranger replied.

'How d'ye ken what we're at?' Donald's surprise made him lapse into even broader Scots; then, as the man went on, suspicion replaced surprise.

'There were a bloke from Scotland used to camp in them trees.' He pointed with his fishing-rod to a copse on the other bank. 'Every three years or so 'e come pearl-fishing, though 'e's not been for near five year now. Bin comin' 'ere for nigh on twenty years, all told.'

With a secret, knowing look, Donald asked: 'Was he a wee, stocky man wi' dark curly hair?' His expression turned to one of grim satisfaction before the fisherman had finished confirming his suspicion. 'Kent it, Neily! Kent it! Wullie's fished it for years.'

Willy Abernethy, to whom I'd written after seeing him on TV, lived only five miles from Donald and Neil and was a sort of arch-rival. Donald seemed to be almost delighted that we were fishing Willy's left-overs. So much for our being the first for four hundred years!

Though shells weren't particularly abundant, they were large, and a high proportion of them were crooks. It was easy to see how the Irt gained its reputation. I saw pearls that day that I have hardly seen the like of since, though later that year Neil took a twenty-seven-grain 'drop' from the Irt: a lustrous, peachy-coloured pearl the shape, and almost the size, of a wren's egg.

Sadly, the Irt's mussels are almost extinct and wouldn't recover even with rigorous protection.

From the Irt, we headed south along the edge of the high country, then cut inland across Corney Fell towards Morecambe Bay. We had to reach the Lune before dark to see if it was worth staying the night there. Weary from driving, the early start and the excitement of some real fishing, each of us seemed lost in our thoughts, but the sight of the River Lune rid us of self-analysis. We approached it down a long, wooded hill just outside Caton and could see a sharp turn in the river's course as it hit the steep slope we were descending.

'That must be "The Crook o' Lune",' I said to Donald.

'There'll be plenty o' good crooks here then?' he added. He and Neil were great believers in omens and signs.

Just before the village we crossed the river on a side road and parked at the end of the bridge. As soon as we entered the water, hundreds of shells stared up at us from between black rocks. Most of them were dead, still in their natural positions, half buried in the sand. A few could be seen to be alive by a frill of mantle protruding from the slightly open valves. The absence of shells in the middle of the river was puzzling. The journal stated that they occurred right across the river and were 'easily reached by wading'. Only a strip up the west bank contained any, and three-quarters of those were dead. I believe they were fished almost to extinction, then a spillage of poisonous chemical finished off most of those that remained.

In the long summer twilight we drove east, across the Pennines, passing through villages strangely deserted and along roads devoid of traffic. Apparently the last car in Britain, we passed neither car nor pedestrian for miles. Amid the grey desolation of bleak, twilit moorland, in a no-man's-land between Lancashire and Yorkshire, a stark row of stone cottages protruded abruptly from the bare roadside. The fact that they faced south did nothing to soften their aspect. Harshly incongruent in the soft colours dusk laid gently on the rounded hills, their asymmetry was accented by a lack of buildings on the other side of the road.

Neil saw none of this. His attention was focussed on the nearest building. He swung the car in to the side, and we read the sign 'The Moorcock Inn'.

'It's a pub, ged!' he shouted. 'What a void it's in.'

After a rustling of hair being raked with fingers, and crumbs and cigarette ash dusted from clothes, we scrambled out. The bar was empty, but we were so glad to leave the car that our own company sufficed. A small, stooped old man came wheezing from the room behind the bar to serve; Davy and Neil fed the fruit machine and juke box, and the place came to life.

A few nips and half pints later, we found we had a liberal host. A heavy two-way traffic flowed across the bar. The landlord was over seventy, and not in the best of health, but he really entered into the spirit of things, reminiscing on his youthful beer-drinking. We doubted he'd last another Pennine winter, yet four years later, in our local paper, we read that the landlord of 'The Moorcock Inn' and his wife, well known to hill-walkers in the Pennines, had died in bed when the inn was gutted by fire. Both were in their seventies. We left the inn so late that we camped in the first gateway where lush grass disguised railway metal bottoming. Andy and I were as oblivious to the discomfort as we were to Davy's snoring. Neil, kept awake by petrol fumes in the back of the car, lay smoking till sleep overtook him.

Despite the previous night's damage, we rose at first light, broke camp and drove on without washing or eating. We bought freshly baked pies in Pickering, then looked in the nearby River Derwent. In clear, chalky water we saw some broken valves of duck mussels. Following a small tributary of the Derwent northwards, the car climbed the south-western edge of the North York Moors, passing the futuristic, yet obsolete domes of the early warning radar at Fylingdales Moor, and descended into Eskdale by tiny, steep lanes.

We worked our way up the River Esk to Leaholme, looking at any accessible stretches, but found nothing among gravel and rock, the only bottom available. Crowds of picnickers on the banks, and on the green by Leaholme Bridge, meant it must be the weekend: we'd lost track of time. To the older men and women in the throng, whose only concession to the midday heat was to roll up their sleeves, we hardly merited a glance. However, our green body-waders, jugs and long tangs, and the old sacks swinging at our sides, drew a range of responses from sniggering to disbelief from the younger members of the crowd.

Right away I found three shells in water clouded by the feet of curious children and dogs paddling alongside me. Neil, Andy and Davy went downstream, and Donald and I fished a quiet pool near the bridge.

The Esk produced a couple of pearls each, and there was enough fishing to make it worth another visit. With about two hours' daylight left, we made for the last river on the list. We'd not eaten since early morning in Pickering, and there was little left in the car. The North York Moors were hardly bristling with chip shops, and it wasn't till we reached the outskirts of Guisborough that we saw one. It was so big I thought it was a furniture store at first. With our appetites sharpened by hunger, the chips were glorious; not my usual adjective for greasy food. They banished the dullness that had crept over us, and we pushed on into Northumberland, keen to reach the river before dark.

The light held as we came down the long, steep hill to the River.[1] A short distance down from a side road that followed the river for a few hundred yards, we pulled onto a grassy verge where river and road parted company, and pulled on our waders.

'It's cassied,[2] ged!' shouted Neil, first in the water.

'Aye, but they're red-rotten beaks,' countered Donald to stifle any excess of enthusiasm.

A minute later Neil yelled back: 'They may be beaks, but they're throwing pearls. I'd a couple o' crooks straight off, an' ain o' them's got a bonny wee button in it.'

It was plain to see who had the 'easy' waders now. I had barely got to the water when the others were starting to come out. In the translucent dusk we changed and cleaned up a bit. The pub at the bridge beckoned.

[1] Omitted to protect last English pearl river.

[2] Full, packed.

Once in, we rapidly blended with a crowd of local people, and the landlord forgot to look at the clock. It was well after midnight when we went back to the grassy corner to put up the tent in the dark. As usual, Neil and Donald slept in the car, where they could get bedded down more quickly. Andy, Davy and I could hear muttered complaints of a smell of petrol long after we were settled.

The expected hangover had still not materialized, and we in the tent woke refreshed to the sound of muttering and coughing from the car, having slept through it on the softest grass so far. Someone found a few eggs and a tin of beans in the car. The partially mixed eggs were heated in the dirty pan, and the beans slopped in on top of them. The resulting sludge was swallowed half-cooked.

Below the camp we stopped to look at the river. 'I like tae see a burn like that,' Neil said with satisfaction. 'Pool and stream, time aboot.' This meant long pools separated by shallow rushes, in the pearl-fishers' parlance.

Donald and I settled on a couple of pools about a quarter of a mile from the car. The bottom was covered with a silt of dead weed and peat that Donald called 'soup'. It was very quiet fishing the calm water. I got a couple of nice pearls at the first opening, then, after another half an hour, came out with a bag of shells that could hardly be lifted up the steep bank. For the number of shells there were not many pearls, but another two or three were added to the bottle, and I sat back contentedly and looked round for a while.

The hilltops were covered in blooming heather and bathed in a soft summer light. I could feel the depth of the silence. It sharpened the small sounds of running water, the tired drone of heavy flies, and the drift of talk from the others, a couple of hundred yards away. I lay back in the long grass and let the sounds grow fainter, while the hazy sunlight warmed me gently. Occasionally a louder noise, a curlew calling from the hill behind or the expressionless bleat of a sheep, would bring the world back into focus for a few seconds, then it slipped away again.

Time was an intruder in the pearl-fisher's day: it passed unnoticed till the empty stomach, the bent back or the waning light reminded us of its passing. Sitting by the river that August day, I felt, at long last, that what I was doing was right. It needed no soul-searching explanation or justification. I was alive and couldn't ask more of life than it was giving me.

The car had carried nearly a thousand pounds of flesh and bone, and almost as much again of luggage, up hills sometimes steeper than one in four. Worn propshaft joints were causing vibration, an intolerable drone that was felt rather than heard. That, and shortage of food and money, made Donald and Neil decide to go home that night. They dropped me at the tent, and though they were supposed to be coming back, I wondered if I would see them again.

After a solitary meal, I walked to the pub. The landlord asked me to join him and his wife and some friends in their lounge and would not let me pay for a round of drinks. The pleasant evening filled the gap left by the sudden departure of my friends, and the tent had a homely air, from being in the same place for two nights. However, it was still strange fishing alone the next day, and miserable weather did little to help. The only good crook I found contained a huge, dull, fawn ball. Bitterly disappointed after the excitement of finding it, I went to the tent to eat.

Later I fished up past the bridge to an old packhorse bridge, accompanied by two boys who told me they'd seen pearl-fishers at Black Burn. I assumed this was another river, but it turned out to be the local name for a deep pool where people swam in hot weather, and lay just ahead. A party of children, including my two friends, had been prevented from swimming in that part of the river the year before. Two men turned them back, but my friends sneaked past, and saw divers in the water. When they'd gone, the black mass of mussels, long taken for granted as part of the bottom, were gone. Looking in off the edge of a low waterfall, I saw nothing but bare sand.

This was the first time I had heard of such a thing. Nowadays it is commonplace. Divers from the Perth Sub Aqua Club and many university diving clubs took to pearl-fishing. They exterminated the shells in pools that even the most adept boat fishers could not see. When the shallows are wiped out, these places, though not the ideal breeding ground for mussels, restocked the shallow 'nursery' beds in the rushes. They formed safe breeding reservoirs, and their absence means several rivers are going to become extinct when the adults that remain are dead. Ironically, the deeps are not even good pearl beds. The only way they are made to pay is by lifting a large number of mussels quickly. The diver can do this and return to the bottom while a colleague opens them. Several hundredweight can be taken on one tank of air. 'Kill more' is the motto.

The peculiar thing about this river was that nobody else seemed to have fished it. We found such an abundance of mussels on our first visit that it didn't seem to tie in with the story of the divers. Could anyone have been that shortsighted? To have fished the only really deep pool and ignored all the easy water seemed ludicrous to us. Even our rival Bill Abernethy seemed, for once, to have missed out on this river.

When the others didn't return as planned, I felt a bit deflated and, after a quiet drink, turned in.

At the village shop, the next morning, I met one of our acquaintances from the pub. Archie Catto was a well-spoken man of about sixty, with an interest in local history. Like the others we'd met, and like so many people who live by pearl rivers, he had no idea such things went on. He invited me to lunch to see round his old stone farmhouse with its adze-hewn roof beams, and the church nearby, which he believed had a gate from the nearby Roman camp built into it. This passed a dull, drizzly afternoon. Then, on my way back to the tent; Archie pulled up abruptly at the pub. Andra's rotund figure waved excitedly from the car-park entrance. Most of the car-park was taken up by a huge, gold Oldsmobile. Standing agape at the vast expanse of bonnet, wondering what manner of beast lurked beneath it, I was reduced to stating the obvious. 'Your car's arrived.'

We went into the bar, where Donald, Neil, Davy and Wee Andy had been welcomed back with open arms and drink was 'fleein' a' roads', as they put it.

Neil took me aside and handed me a £10 note for my share of the pearls, little though my contribution had been. I had more money at that point than I'd set off with nearly a month earlier, and had spent a fortune. The pace of life had been so fast that money had just passed through my hands like dust. I never looked to see what petrol cost or what a round of drinks was doing to my wallet, I just handed it over and got on without caring. This was living. Sitting at home with an odd pound to spare, counting, counting and recounting to see if some paltry item could be managed, belonged to another world and to the person I used to be. Sometimes, when I looked at the pearls in the bottle, I couldn't understand how a quarter of an ounce of calcium carbonate crystals could feed that car, and two large families, and let us all run about the country like a bunch of outlaws.

I cannot disgrace the word 'breakfast' with what we ate the next morning, but all faced it with no trace of queasiness, then headed briskly downstream to the day's business. Donald and I tried the big shells in the deep pools again, and Andra fished below us, with the rest further downstream. It was a perfect day again, and I couldn't resist lying back luxuriously in the warm sun, listening to the ebb and flow of small sounds in the soft breeze. That we were going our separate ways at the end of the day's fishing didn't bother me. It was good to savour the moment without marring it with the concerns of a future which, at the time, seemed distant.

Donald and I, hoping for big pearls in the pools, had little success and went to see how Andra had fared. He'd gone downstream to meet the other three, leaving neat little piles of open shells on the rocks beside the shallow rapids he'd fished. The rest had scorned these 'streams' as 'useless backbreakers'.

We found Andra sitting watching Davy, Neil and Andy, who were standing wearily in another stream about nine inches deep. Neil spotted us. 'Donald, deek the pearls Andra's got in the wee streams. We've been fishing dungeons[1] all day for devil[2] a hait, ged.'

We crossed to see. Andra held out his bottle. There were a dozen beautiful pearls rolling round in it – well over £50 worth and almost as much in weight as the rest put together.

'Wee Andy' Stewart hauled himself despairingly up the bank with a huge bag of shells. 'I havnae got a seed the hale day.' He kept us waiting, opening his shells with Donald, who could never resist going through other people's shells to see if they had any good crooks. He put a few aside for Andy to keep till the end. Andy became more and more downhearted as he got to the bottom of the bag. Then, with a cry of relief, he opened his last shell to reveal a beautiful little button.

It was a long walk to the car. We changed and had a standing meal of cold baked beans from the tin, and bread and cheese. My

[1] Deep, steep sided pools.
[2] Nothing.

dandelion leaf garnish caused some amusement. Apart from an odd orange, it was the first fresh food I'd eaten all week. The pearl-fishers' diet, away from home, is somewhat akin to that which led to scurvy in the days of the sailing ship.

We went for a last drink. I never expected to see Andra again, as he was returning to Canada in the autumn. We'd got on well in the brief interval since our meeting. Though nothing had been arranged, I did expect to see the others the following spring.

After the big car had vanished over the hill, I stood beside the empty road for a while, then turned and walked down the moonlit lane by the river, reflecting on what had been the most exciting episode of my life so far.

Next morning I packed about eighty pounds of gear into the rucksack, then got it on my back. With the banjo on my shoulder, the autoharp tucked under my arm, the guitar and fiddle were carried by their case handles in my free hand. Like this, I managed to reach the main road without becoming aware of the impossibility of going any distance. Within ten minutes, two Danish girls in a tiny Citroën, already laden with their own camping equipment, picked me up. My load brought the car to its knees.

I got home late the following evening with a headache, blisters and wrenched shoulder muscles. In my pocket was £32: £2 more than I had left with, plus pearls that subsequently fetched £50, and memories to last a lifetime.

The £52 profit alone was more than a month's wages at the job I had left the previous year. In a month away, I'd spent more on food, drink and fuel than in a normal six months. What was more, I was still a beginner.

People still ask what made me become a pearl-fisher, as though it must, by its very nature, involve sacrifice. I have searched in vain in myself for these sacrifices. If anyone made them, in later years it was my wife.

Unable to wait till spring, I decided to use my new knowledge on the rivers of Devon in late autumn. There had obviously been a drought, as the water in the south-west was very low. Following the River Exe north, thick algal growth in the slow, shallow water failed to disguise the absence of mussels, even in the precise places given by my journal.

I left the Exe. It is added to the long list of extinct rivers we have now. Bishop's Tawton on the River Taw was next in the book, but I was dismayed to find it was in the tidal reach of the river. The journal was precise, but all the other literature said that pearl mussels were not tolerant of salt or brackish water. I dismissed the journal's data as mistaken, yet years later we found many instances of pearl mussels living in tidal water. There is no doubt of their intolerance of salt, so fresh water must lie below the incoming tide. Possibly its cooler temperature creates a strong enough temperature gradient to keep the brackish water from mixing for several miles.

The tide was in, so I started fishing above it at Newbridge and left the rest till low water in the morning. I'd learned in Scotland that one type of 'good bottom' was sand and small stones with algae on them. A mile of careful fishing on this type of bottom produced two shells. Someone had beaten me to it.

With high tide came dusk. It was a lovely evening and still too early to turn in, so I went to the pub in Bishop's Tawton and got talking to some fishermen. They told me they'd seen shells like those I had with me in the river directly across the fields from the pub.

In the morning I decided to see who was right and nearly got stuck in tidal mud while trying to reach the fresh water in the middle of the channel. It was useless and dangerous without help at hand, so I gave up and went to the Torridge.

The upper valley of the Torridge looked fine to me but I saw no mussels. Just before dark I had a quick look near Great Torrington. The valley of the Torridge is heavily wooded here, and fading light would normally have made it impossible for an inexperienced fisher to find an odd shell in the shade of trees at dusk, among the black stones of the river bed. I needn't have worried. A mass of mussels carpeted the bottom. I filled a bag rapidly at random but didn't find any crooks.

The steep valley sides and dense woods left no room for the tent, so I slept in the car in a roadside quarry. First the police wakened me while investigating my 'abandoned car', then torrents of hail and rain drummed on the roof all night. In the morning it was so cold that the hail still lay nearly an inch deep.

I went down to the river and found I didn't need my jug or stick. Groups of mussels sat in less than six inches of water, and I was able to walk along and pick them up with my hands. The rain, however, was unrelenting. I went to the car to eat and put on thigh-waders to make bending less tiring. After eight hours' continuous downpour I had four nice pearls, one a beautiful silver-grey ball nearly a quarter of an inch across.

Dog-tired, I slept in the quarry again, the rain lashing the car till the early hours. I looked at the river in the morning sunshine. It was as though a dam had burst. Where there had been six inches of water, there was now eight feet of roaring brown sludge, bearing trees and dead sheep towards Bideford at high speed. I went back to Exeter to spend the night with friends, and the Exe was in a similar state. Pearl-fishing was at end for the season.

6. How We 'Did' the South-West

The winter dragged on in a succession of odd jobs, brightened only by correspondence with Neil. In March he wrote asking me to meet them at 'The Swan' in Almondsbury, near Bristol, close to his mother's home. They reckoned that, if I could find pearls in Devon, they were lying around for the taking.

When I arrived at 'The Swan', there was no sign of the blue Wolseley, but when I went in, three faces turned towards me. Neil, Donald and Davy Bell jumped up and pumped my hand, clapping me on the back like a long lost friend. A 'nip' of whisky and a pint of beer appeared instantly before me, and we sat round a big table talking excitedly about the rivers I'd seen. It was good to talk 'shop' again. I'd had nobody to share my experiences with, and now I was being consulted about the bottom, the 'class' of shell and all the things I barely knew about the rivers yet but which might tell them something useful to whet their appetites.

We stayed at Neil's mother's and set off very early next morning, leaving my car behind. The part of the Torridge where I got pearls didn't impress them much, but the stretch by the old bridge where I had found nothing caused a bit of excitement. Donald found shells right away. Only two or three, yet one had two nice pearls in it.

Lack of shells forced them to give up. 'The guid bit's aye fished oot,' lamented Donald on the way back to the car. It was their opinion that the bottom end of the river where shells were so common was in that state only because of the rockier bottom and higher water speed reducing the incidence of pearls. Fishers soon gave up these places for more lucrative stretches.

Leaving the Torridge in a south-westerly direction, we intercepted the Tamar near Launceston, where the journal stated that two mussels had been found fifty years before. We found two. With our luck they were probably the same ones.

Recent information on the mussels of the Tamar points to the same reasons for its virtual extinction as the Dart and Taw. There is a remnant population in the river, whose whereabouts will have to remain as secret as it is possible to keep such things. It is so small, and situated in such a way, that it is obviously (to us) a leftover from gross overfishing. Lack of sign of dead mussels points to the same fisher in all these cases.

We crossed Bodmin Moor to the Camel but found that river devoid of evidence of mussels. The south-west is such a small area, and its rivers are so close together, that it would be quite feasible for one man to find all the mussel beds and eradicate them.

In the chip shop in Wadebridge we attracted curious stares, with green body-waders and old sacks hanging at our sides. We were so weary of driving, walking and disappointment that we sat as we were in the shop to eat. We'd 'done' Devon and Cornwall in a day!

Heading back to Bristol along the north coast, the road seemed to go round in circles, and we went in and out of Lynmouth three times before escaping, then stopped at the first roadside inn, too weary and confused to carry on. No tourists were abroad, and the landlord sat with us, 'standing his hand' till one in the morning, then offered us a campsite and use of washing facilities.

In the morning, Neil worked on Donald, persuading him that it was too soon to go home. They'd hardly covered the petrol costs, and there were rivers in South Wales that were virtually on the way home.

The Wye at Symond's Yat was like the Honiton bypass on a Bank Holiday. Unable even to park, we kept going towards the Welsh border. In a quiet lane beyond Hereford, river and road met. I put on the easy waders. Donald once again pointed out the place to look, and a solitary pearl mussel lay beneath his stick. Shells were supposed to have been common in the Wye, though they were said to be very small when fully grown and were usually badly eroded. Possibly the water was almost at the limit of acidity they could stand, and stunted growth, yet below where the alkaline River Lugg enters, no shells are found. We found no more at all.

The Teifi is a beautiful river to a pearl-fisher, and the mussels were pinpointed exactly. In a deep corner below rapids Neil found one lovely shell, but the rest of the river produced only a bloated coypu carcass, and disappointment. We managed to find a campsite and, coming unexpectedly on the A40, pitched the tent on a broad verge. By now I was so accustomed to Davy's snoring that it drowned the noise of big lorries heading for the container terminal at Milford Haven, without disturbing me.

The River Cleddau at Haverfordwest had all the appearance of a pearl stream but we couldn't raise a single shell as we had in the Wye and Teifi. Five or six years later I heard the story of this river. My wife, daughter and I were just back from the second 'Great North American Pearl Fishing Fiasco' (see p.173) and Donald, Neil and some of my in-laws had gone to a nearby hotel, leaving the ladies in the house. We were discussing 'business' and were joined by a man who used to go on trips with Bill Abernethy, who had overheard our pearl talk. He told us of their visit to Pembrokeshire. 'Wully' was looking for a long shot – a river he was told of in Wales, described only as having rhododendron bushes growing by it! In the search they crossed the Western Cleddau. Looking over the bridge, they saw shells lying thick and could even seen crooks among them. They fished it for a few days, getting a lot of small pearls, sometimes two or three in one shell, then left to look for the other river. Not finding it, they continued homeward.

We were fishing two or three years after them, and found nothing. Neil went there in 1978, just a month after we heard this story. He couldn't even find a dead shell; then, as he climbed out of the water to rest, he cut his hand on a shell splinter half buried in the bank. More determined than ever, he fished on and found thirty survivors in three miles of river. When they die, the river's mussels are truly extinct. In a sense it was already extinct. Those thirty mussels, and a few others Neil will have missed, are so few and so far apart that they can never breed.

With heavy hearts we turned east again to the Towy. Though it was a big river, we no longer held out much hope. A few miles above Carmarthen we stopped at the exact spot the journal dictated and found nothing.

Thoroughly dispirited, we went grimly towards certain failure: the Swansea Canal. The chance of pearl mussels being in a canal was remote enough, but in a South Wales valley impossible. The canal turned out to be a kind of mill race which could have supported mussels if they had ever been in the river that fed it. Its source was a dam upriver. The canal poured through numerous breaches in its banks, back into the polluted River Tawe, and left behind it a dried-up ditch full of old prams and bike frames.

One more polluted river lay between us and the Severn bridge; then we went back to Neil's mother's for the night. In the morning Neil was still not happy about going home. He persuaded Donald that the rivers in North Wales, and one in Shropshire, were also virtually on the way home. I decided to go as far as Rhyl with them, and Davy rode with me for company.

The River Clun runs off a strange moorland plateau in west Shropshire. In the middle of the nineteenth century it was mentioned in a periodical *Pearls and Pearling Life*. Whatever it's reputation, we found no evidence of it at any of the places we looked.

'Too wee and too easy fished,' was Donald's opinion. 'This'll be the burn Wully [Abernethy] fished twenty years ago. Wiped oot ged.'

Neil hauled himself out of a narrow, deep stretch he thought might have a few shells left in it. 'There's devil a hait noo anyway. It was probably cassied* when Wully got it.'

We pushed on up the Severn Valley towards the River Dee at Llangollen. According to my journal, the Dee mussels once ranged from Bala Lake to Bangor in Cheshire, a distance of about forty miles of river. It was a big river too, and we hoped we'd get more than one day's fishing. Bridge-hopping, we looked in five or six different places, some of them with such a perfect bottom that we expected to see shells at any moment. In a stream above Llangollen Donald and I came on one dead mussel. We fished right to Bala before giving up, then continued northwards to the Conway Valley, past the spoil heaps of the great slate quarries of Blaenau Ffestiniog. Entering the valley from the south brought us first to the wild upper reaches of the Conway, then the lower river which begins at Waterloo Bridge. The big pool near the station at Bettws-y-Coed proved to be a lucky strike. It was the last refuge of the Conway shells and the upper limit of their former range.

The Conway was one of the most famous of British pearl rivers.

* Full of shells.

From about a mile above the old bridge at Llanrwst, up to Bettws-y-Coed was the pearl mussel's range. The eighteenth-century writer Sir Thomas Pennant relates that as many as sixteen pearls were taken from one shell in the Conway, a record which I came close to that day. The domain of Gwydir, above the bridge at Llanrwst, is thought to be where Sir Richard Wynne (of Gwydir) obtained a fine pearl which he presented to the queen of King Charles II.

Typically of the Welsh, they seem to have kept their pearls to themselves. Apart from the Conway, I have found only a fleeting reference to its tiny neighbour the Ogwen, now extinct, yet there must have been fisheries on at least half a dozen other rivers. To this day, coracle fishers hold salmon-fishing rights that have been handed down for generations. If these men didn't fish pearls, nobody did. I did hear of a television programme in which one of these men admitted to knowing of river pearls, but it would have taken a spell on the rack to get him to say any more on 'the English television'.

We were lucky. Teetering on rocks along the edge of a deep, slow pool, we looked out onto a silt-covered sand where an occasional huge shell sat side on to us. Some hid beneath overhangs facing away from us and could not be reached. Side on, shells are very hard to raise. The long stick is clumsy at full stretch and usually has to be placed almost straight down on the narrowest angle of the shell, otherwise it merely knocks them out of the bottom and they lie on their side. This is fine if you can wedge them between your feet and make another stab, but if they are seven or eight feet away, in five feet of water or more, it is a time-consuming business. The shell has to be dragged nearer. Failing to lift it pushed it further away again. I struggled this way with one mussel while the others were gathering them steadily. When I finally bagged it, it was a short, rumpled shell with many finely divided growth rings: an old crook.

Donald had passed me on the outside. His waders were higher than mine and enabled him to reach more shells, not to mention the skill with which he manipulated his tangs. The shells themselves caused problems. They were the biggest any of us had ever seen. The tangs had to be set wide to accommodate them. 'What a crook!' Donald was prodding at a shell at full stretch. I didn't know how he could see it was a crook. When I looked out to where his stick was dragging it nearer, it just looked like any other shell to me.

'Ged! What a savver!' The meaning of this new word soon came when the stench of putrid mussel reached my nostrils. Donald climbed out immediately to open his shells and get at the rotten crook. I joined him. My crook had fourteen pearls in it. Six were what the pearl-fishers called 'stickers', seven were brown, and one was white and pear-shaped. Stickers are pearls that are buried in the shell and, like brown ones, are of no value, unless they can be detached. (They are sometimes called 'blister' pearls in the sea fisheries.)

'There's twa bonny balls in the deid crook,' Donald called out. He held them out for me to see. One was the largest pearl I'd seen yet, but it didn't excite Donald that much. There was a stain caused by the rotten flesh on both pearls, which may have caused his lack of enthusiasm.

'Och, that'll clean up, nae bother,' Neil assured him.

'Aye, we'll try the spirits on it,' Donald agreed.

'Spirits of salt', hydrochloric acid, dilute, are capable of removing organic stains or minor blemishes on the surface of pearls. Deeper-seated problems are only made worse by attempts to improve them in this way. The acid eats more rapidly into the faulty areas and turns them into pits which cannot be disguised.

The shells soon petered out but a good weight of pearls had been taken from this one pool. It must have been a fantastic river when shells were plentiful. We tried other parts, but even some of the older references of the Conway stated that pearls were found only in the deeps or where shells survived among thick weed.*

Crossing the ancient bridge at Llanrwst, we had a roadside meal before going our separate ways. I took the opportunity to visit my cousins on the coast, where I'd spent so many holidays as a child, and Donald, Neil and Davy were going home via the Irt, from which they took some more fine pearls.

I took my time going south. Another look in the Clun didn't tell me any more than the first. The early spring down in the south made it very hard to delay going to Scotland again, and it was obvious that that was where I was going.

* Now totally extinct.

7. Old Rattray Style

I nearly went mad with frustration as winter dragged its heels into April. Unable to wait, tent, sleeping-bag, fiddle, banjo, guitar, autoharp and a bag of pearl-fishing gear were stuffed into the old Austin, and I set off for Blairgowrie. If Blairgowrie had been in Australia, I couldn't have been heading for a more drastic change in my life.

Twilight crept across the hills behind the town as I crossed the bridge between Blairgowrie and Rattray and pulled into the yard in Yeaman Street. It was more like coming home than leaving it. Both houses spilled their human contents into the yard. Neil, Donald, the two Marys, their seven children and 'Wee Andy' milled round, bombarding me with questions. I couldn't recall being made so welcome anywhere. I was dragged from house to house and fed tea and rolls till they came out of my ears. Andy was showing me how his mandolin playing had improved since we last met when Neil arrived and dragged me away to 'The George' to met Davy Bell and other pearling acquaintances from the previous year.

The bar of 'The George' was basic, its functions being the serving and consumption of alcohol. However, I was introduced to so many people there that night that the obsolete British Rail Southern Region décor passed unnoticed. At ten-fifteen the flashing blue light of a police car outside reminded the landlord that it was five minutes after time. A dozen or more men trooped back to Neil's house bearing their share of a 'kerry-oot'.

In the early hours of the morning, when the noisy crowd dispersed, I was going to put up my tent in the garden, but Neil and Mary wouldn't hear of it and told me to use the bed-settee in the living-room. I slept diagonally across it to stop my feet hanging out of the bottom.

The weather had been cold and showery before my arrival and continued to delay the start of the pearl-fishing for some time. Although I was confined to the house for much of the time, my new surroundings were fascinating, and there was no rush now.

To me, life in Yeaman Street was a kaleidoscope of faces and a cacophony of voices with a mixture of strange accents. The door of Neil's living-room opened and closed so many times in the course of a day that, in cold weather, it would have been better tearing it from its hinges and burning it in the middle of the floor to keep the room warm. A sheet of polythene had been pinned to the wall by the door to prevent the wallpaper becoming shiny from the rubbing of shoulders.

Nobody knocked before they came into the house. Often, the doors of both houses were hanging wide, televisions blared, a light blazed and an electric fire heated an empty room. A visitor might wait ten minutes for everyone to walk round the corner, or all day for them to come back from Perth. A knock at the door meant either strangers, or THE AUTHORITIES, and a hush fell over the household while Neil (or Donald, who had the same system) rose to see who it was. Open house and complete lack of privacy caused none of the neurotic behaviour that most people would develop in similar circumstances. Cookers and kettles steamed day-long to provide meals and drinks for an ever-changing populace.

The yard between the houses was as much a part of the social scene as the houses themselves. In good weather it was the meeting place for everyone concerned with pearl-fishing, and for friends and relatives of both families. Groups of men lounged against parked cars or gathered by the doors of the houses, through which a stream of children passed, endlessly making their way from one house to the other.

The 'Two Marys' either brought out tea or invited everyone in for 'meat'. The men in this gathering played the part of hunters or warriors, apart from the women, discussing matters of great import as though standing round an imaginary camp fire.

Four sons in Neil's house and two boys and a girl in Donald's, dozens of visitors each week, coupled with a casual disregard for material things meant considerable wear and tear on furnishings. New replacements could have swallowed the men's entire earnings from pearl-fishing, so nearly everything was replaced at least once a year from the local auction sales. In fact, visitors to Rowan Cottage and Holly Cottage were often more at ease than they could be in their own homes, and the wives of some of the men who got into trouble for spending so much time there would have done well to ask themselves why. There was no danger of the tools of daily life such as cars, furniture or washing machines becoming objects of admiration or, worse still, a source of worry. They were consumed, then replaced as cheaply as possible: sacrificed freely in the interests of a free and easy life.

As well as sometimes acting as slides and climbing frames for children, the cars often had to carry almost the entire complement of one house, and a couple of hangers-on from the other, every time it moved. The rest of the time it transported up to half a dozen men and their pearling gear several hundred miles over some of the worst roads in the country. Driving away from one river and heading for another, we sat in the car in wet waders with water running from the overboots, amongst an accumulation of cigarette ash, mud and the debris of hasty meals eaten on the move. Neil remarked drily, 'Oor cars rot fae the inside, oot.'

Once, two hundred miles from home and thirty from the nearest garage, the rear leaf spring of the old Wolseley snapped right through, leaving the axle on that side trailing, and the car's body sagging drunkenly. They excavated the 'tool kit' from under waders, old socks and tins of food. It comprised a claw hammer, a pair of pliers, a wheelbrace and a worn-out adjustable spanner. Roadside fencewires was cut with the pliers, and the wheel nuts were removed with the wheelbrace. Three men lifted the car while the wheel was taken off; then they set it down on a rock while work was in progress. The broken spring leaves were bound with wire, and the wheel was replaced. The car sat level but developed a crab-like gait when driven as the leaves slid out of the binding. A rock was torn from a drystone dyke, and the car was reversed into it to shove the wheel forward. A loop of wire was led from the axle to a cross-member further forward, and tightened by winding it with a strong stick. It worked, and the clawhammer and spanner were not even needed. The wire loop stretched under the load eventually, till drivers behind, alarmed at the diagonal angle we had to our direction of motion, tooted their horns. This was our signal to get another boulder with which to ram the axle back in line, and to retighten the wire. There was no thought of going to a garage, other than for petrol, and the total lack of concern was confirmed by the fact that another day's fishing was squeezed in on the way home.

In season, or out, daily life for the pearl-fishing families was a loose series of random events. Like 'idle rich', they'd no framework of working week and weeknd. One pleasure resulting from this was having time to talk without one party having previous engagements that lead to a glance-at-the-watch syndrome, letting you know they have more important things to do than talk to you. Also, if long-absent friends appeared unexpectedly and sat till the arly hours over a bottle or two, there was no fidgeting as midnight approached. The weather could change the following day's plans more than a hangover, and one day had no more avantage than another. In this way, nothing was lost that couldn't be regained.

When it came to pearl-fishing, however, things got done. An uncharacteristic punctuality became apparent. In the final minutes of preparation before leaving for a river, small delays caused irritation, and bigger hold-ups were seen as an omen of a bad day.

Wives were not without justification when they said, 'Ye'll dae anything tae get tae the burn, but a wee job aboot the hoose cannae be done.' Neil's comment on trivial (to him) household chores was, 'There's nae gain in it.'

Though it was a male-dominated world in many respects, and the women's place was in the home 'watching bairns and makin' meat', the two Marys' resistance was tersely illustrated by Mary McCormick's counter-punching remark: 'I ken my place, Neily, but I'll no bide in it.'

Like the trawlermen who leave, with all hopes hinging on a good catch, for a place their wives will probably never see, our departure was tinged with uncertainty. This was more apparent some years later, after a friend drowned while at the Spey with us. For us, torn between the women's nagging doubts and the supercharged excitement of setting out, it was like an actor's first night nerves: we never got over it.

A good day's fishing had to be celebrated, a poor one was reason for rest and refreshment. These feeble excuses often kept us out till he dawn chorus began. Full of drunken bravado, we'd stagger in the door, gaze round the company of dozing wives who often kept vigil in Neil's living-room, and any man who called himself a man would bark, 'Werzma meat, woman?' It had to be done with the righteous indignation of a man who's had a hard day and night, while his wife has dozed at the fireside. You'd be sure to get it immediately, if you could see to catch it.

All Donald and Neil's work depended on good weather. Scottish weather meant that they spent more time at home than most men. On wet days, or when the water was high, Neil and Mary and I might be sitting talking. The children of both families often watched television together, the seven of them lying in a tangle on the floor. Donal would suddenly burst in roaring, 'D'ye see that the noo? The government's gi'in' some moich opera hoose hundreds o' thoosands o' pounds. What use is that tae us, ged?' During the nsuing argument, the children slyly increased the volume of the television to match the adults' din till Neil had to roar, 'Put that voice doon!' As soon as the children knew no one would notice, the cycle began again. Eventually I learned how to filter either the television or the speaker from the rest.

With so many visitors to Yeaman Street, my appreciation of the Scots' language, its richness and variety, grew rapidly. I soon began to recognize the differences that occurred within fifteen miles of Blairgowrie. Within twenty miles there are four distinct accents. My wife claims to differentiate between Alyth and Blair, a distance of less than five miles.

The local accent differs markedly from the sing-song Fife tongue, the flat, dry Forfar and Kirriemuir speech to the north-east, and the wise-cracking cynicism of the Dundonians. Then there are the 'travellers' (see p.98). They use many words and phrases totally their own, some which have roots in Gaelic, some in Scots, and a few of French origin. Others are shared with Romanies. Even without using their dialect words, they can make public conversation private by the staccato, machine-gun delivery of their consonants. Donald was once asked about my job by a Donaldson. 'Hwarz Rid-Peter werkintay?' is about as close as I can get phonetically to 'Who's Red Peter working to?' (for).

There is a saying hereabouts: 'Not worth a tinker's curse.' It does not do justice to their curses. In the heat of an argument, they often run to paragraph length and are more foully unprintable than anything previously imagined: an extravagantly inventive poetry of invective. It is such a pity that their dialect and speed of word make it incomprehensible to most people, and that so much watering down occurs in translation.

8. The Early Season

Our first day's fishing came after a seemingly interminable wait. Donald had got hold of a cheap dinghy and wanted to try it on a couple of deep pools up the Tummel. His faith in it was rather touching.

We set off towards Dunkeld and up Strathtay on a fresh morning. Gusts of winds tore at the still bare branches, and shafts of sunlight raced before the squalls that lashed the valley sides. Below, on our left, the Tay was still running high, but Neil reckoned the water could be clear enough for fishing. The sun followed us through Pitlochry and all along Loch Tummel side when we left the A9. It was still shining when we stopped just above Tummel Bridge to put on our waders and blow up the dinghy.

Donald struggled with the inflated dinghy in the fitful wind, climbing a barbed-wire fence and a wall to reach the water. Neil and I peered into the deep corner where Donald was spinning uncontrollably in the light craft as a squall began to move down the glen. We could see right into the pool, which was about eight feet deep. The bottom was composed of angular boulders, probably thrown down the bank on the corner by a farmer to stop the river eating away his field. There were no shells.

'It's nae use in this gale, ged!' Donald shouted over the shrieking wind. He made for the bank and disappeared among swirling snowflakes. Snow and hail whipped our frozen hands as we clawed our way up the bank. Donald was crouching under the dinghy behind a drystone dyke when the squall really struck. The dinghy simply took off, bounded across the little field and flung itself on the only piece of barbed wire it could find in a break in the wall.

'See that!' Donald shouted after it. 'Made for the wire like a magnet!' He rescued the sagging wreck and we retreated to the car.

There's no more pathetic creature than a pearl-fisher confined to the house by bad weather. Every morning we looked out, hoping for a change. In desperation, Donald and Neil thought the River Lochay at the far end of Loch Tay might be worth looking at. So far into the hills, it often happens that frost continues to hold snow on the hills and prevents the rivers from rising till later in spring. It doesn't make the water any warmer for fishing though. If the Lochay proved useless, we could always try the nearby Dochart, or the upper Tay. It was all new to me.

The convoluted road with its blind bends and hills made the short distance seem longer and more interesting. We headed west, first to Dunkeld, then across the Tay to the quieter road winding along the west side of Strathtay upriver to Aberfeldy. The weather was crisp and clear. Huge mounds of cloud stacked on the high ground were torn by strong winds and shredded over the broad valley. Sunlight broke the shadows along the forested hills on either side of the river's floodplain into shifting blocks of dark and light green.

It was hard for me to grasp that these surroundings were to be my place of work. I didn't want the realization to come too soon, but to leave me plenty of time to relish it. The winding road to the Highland town of Aberfeldy was full of inviting glimpses of the big river set against the wide hills or framed by the old trees on its banks. Each glimpse set Donald and Neil reminiscing on a certain day's fishing, and each day had its particular pearls or incidents that made them memorable. How different from the routine of most people's lives in which the yearly holiday contains the majority of their memories.

'That was a barry stream. Remember the big button Davy got there?'

'Aye, and Big Bink fell doon the bank and broke his jug.'

A little further on: 'We'd over £100 worth oot o' that bit the other year, remember.'

'That bit was never any use, ged! I never made anything o' it in my life.'

'Och, you ken the time we werenae botherin' but Gordon and Dayser persuaded us tae hae an afternoon at the Tay. We couldnae gang wrang, ged. Last time, last year, we got devil a hait in the same bit.'

'Aye, that's recht.'

I listened in silence, watching each new length of sun-dappled road open before us. It would be some years before I could earn a place in these reminiscences.

Beyond Aberfeldy the road followed the river closely for a few miles before climbing round the grounds of Taymouth Castle. On our descent to the foot of Loch Tay at Kenmore we glimpsed the massive building through a gap in the trees. Even though the far end of the loch was hidden by a bend about four miles away, it still looked huge to me. The great mass of Ben Lawers dominated the skyline, its upper slopes covered in fresh snow.

Beyond Kenmore, Ben Lawers towered on our right, lost at times in fierce squalls. Below, on our left, the loch seemed to stretch as far as the eye could see. It was nearly half an hour before we looked down on the far end of it where the rivers Lochay and Dochart meet to form the Tay. We met a lorry heading towards Perth carrying the remains of a light aeroplane that had vanished in the hills months before. The weather had been severe, and things didn't look good for us.

We drove up Glen Lochay, trying to find a good spot to look in. Above the wooded lower glen, a bare, boulder-strewn wilderness had only a shepherd's summer bothy to show the hand of man. We had almost reached the snow-line, and on getting out to look at the river, a raw chill made us gasp. The river was a gravel bed, so we turned back.

On the way back down the glen Donald had a quick dip in a sheltered corner, but the water was 'pure broon' and there was 'nae bottom'.

At the main road we turned towards Killin to get pies. The pearl-fishers liked the convenience of the Scottish pie and bridie and missed them when they were away from home. The bridie is a sort of flaky, pasty-shaped meat pie. They could be bought hot or cold in most places and eaten on the move without cooking or washing up to hinder getting to the next river.

Killin is a little town on the Dochart near the head of Loch Tay. Neil drove through it to let me see the Falls of Dochart. Here the river rages among a series of rocky, pine-covered islands and huge rocks, slides over sheets of rock, and funnels under an old stone bridge. The narrow bridge uses as a stepping-stone an island on which there is an ancient Clan McNab graveyard.

We ate our pies leaning on the bonnet of the car outside the baker's shop watching violent snowstorms on Ben Lawers.

'Ged! How she boils and brews up there,' Donald cackled fiendishly as another squall lashed the hill while we lounged in warm sunshine.

There was no point in trying to fish till the water had dropped and fresh snow had ceased. It had been spring when we were in Devon weeks before, and daffodils were nodding in the woods by the Torridge, but here in the northern hills it was still winter.

While we waited for the weather again, Neil and Mary dressed me in an old kilt and photographed me in the yard amid hoots of laughter from Donald.

'An Englishman, ged! Wi' that red baird he looks mair like a Scot than any o' us. He must be a McGregor, ged!'

Donald, Neil and Gordon Wilson, a Rattray man who had given up a job to go pearling, had been fishing the River Lyon the previous season, just in front of Meggernie Castle. Hidden by a floodbank from the windows of the castle, they were in a good bit, getting plenty of crooks, when an enraged bellow made them jump. A tweed-suited figure levelled a shotgun at them from the bank.

'Dinnae move! We have ye noo! Your car's immobilized and the poalus [police] are on their way.'

'Awa' ye gang, min, an' dinnae be an idiot,' Donald replied with exasperating tolerance.

The man's face went crimson and veins bulged till he looked as if his head was going to explode. Neil had some lovely crooks in his bag and was determined to open them before things got any worse. He disappeared into the bushes on the other bank as the bell tolled in the castle and people began to appear from all directions. Gordon, who'd been programmed not to react to any outside interference, fished on beneath the shotgun barrels, occasionally gazing blankly up at the ranting keeper, then bending over his jug again.

The car had lacked a certain document that would have made it of interest to the police, and they had to get out as there was only one road up the glen. Completely ignoring the blustering threats of the keeper, and the general confusion, they walked deliberately to the car and stowed their gear. Nothing appeared to have been done to it, so they drove quickly down the glen.

So many pearls had been taken in the short time they'd had that they had to return. The plan was for Donald and Neil to fish out of sight of the castle, and Davy and I would take the hot spot. Using my car might disguise things a little more, as the keepers wouldn't know it. Into the boot we put a bucket of shells I'd brought up with me. Since I took them from the Torridge they'd already spent three weeks in the bath at my parents' home. As we left. Gordon arrived so we stopped at his house for his jug and waders.

I took the now almost familiar route by Dunkeld, up Strathtay to Aberfeldy, but this time turned north over the Tay by General Wade's bridge with its statue of Rob Roy McGregor. Beyond the bridge, the road passed between an avenue of huge poplars, then turned sharply westwards towards the highest hills. Passing the massive, derelict Castle Menzies at Weems, in the level floodplain of the Appin of Dull, we entered the rolling landscape of the mouth of Glen Lyon. Beyond the hamlet of Fortingall, the road tightened into a forested ravine through which the river cut a narrow, ragged path.

'That's McGregor's Leap doon there. It's where ane o' Donald's ancestors jumped the burn tae escape the redcoats,' Neil cracked.

Shaded by great beeches, the road clung to the side of the ravine before dropping to the riverside in the upper part of the glen. It was the loveliest place I'd seen, and I still count it as a favourite place to fish, though more for its surroundings than for the pearls, which are scarcely worth a thought. Glen Lyon winds through some of the highest hills in Perthshire. On the north side of the river, facing the sun, is a strip of farmland backed by heather-covered hills with forested slopes. The other side is mostly rough grazing interspersed with forest and, in the part above McGregor's Leap, slopes straight to the river.

At Fortingall, Neil had pointed out a series of thatched cottages which, despite their beauty, looked a little out of place. He told me that there was supposed to have been a Roman camp nearby which gave the village its name, and that Pontius Pilate was said to have been born in it. An ancient yew tree in the churchyard at Fortingall was probably an old tree even at that time. It survives today as a ring of growth around the edge of a ten-foot-wide space which used to be occupied by its main trunks.

Beyond the hamlet of Innerwick the river was smaller. It flowed between a fringe of trees, under the grey stone arches of the Bridge of Balgie and past a tiny post office and store. The road on the other side disappeared into a desolate glen that cut into the side of Ben Lawers, and Neil told me it went over Ben Lawers and down to Loch Tay side. We came to the gate of Meggernie Castle, and the road skirted its grounds, climbing behind a belt of mature Scots pines to avoid intruding on the privacy of its policies.*

'Lord Wills cannae be in residence, or nae doot a' the flags would be fleein',' Donald commented sarcastically, still smarting from his treatment on their last visit.

We changed out of sight of the castle, and Gordon started to follow Davy and me.

'Och, they'll no remember me,' he said reassuringly. 'I'd be as well fishing wi' you boys.'

Neil called out our last instructions from the car. 'Keep by the big dyke till ye get tae the water. Gordon'll ken which bit tae fish, but keep your heids doon behind the floodbank. If anyone cames tae put ye off, just walk awa' fae them. We'll tak' the car and fish further up.'

We cut down the side of a big stone wall that ran through the trees towards the river. Pushing through a thicket at the water's edge, we walked downstream towards an open bank where the scrub and trees had been cleared for salmon-fishers to cast without hindrance. Peeping over the bank, I appreciated our predicament. The castle faced us with a mass of windows directly across open grass. All seemed quiet.

Bending over the jug, I saw it was just as we'd been told. The water was shallow and fairly quick. The bottom was littered with black rocks, and the shells sat, or were wedged between them, in pockets of yellow sand. A lot of the shells were covered in the same slippery green algal growth as the rocks, which made them hard to extract. I'd never seen so many crooks and marked shells. Though excited, we kept comment to a hushed minimum to avoid

* Parkland.

attracting attention.

After our run through the forty yards or so of 'good bottom', we had an opening, hiding in the bushes by the water. With a good few pearls in the bottle, we started again at the beginning.

'The tinks wouldnae fish this bit,' Gordon said as we sat in the trees for our second opening. 'They'd be feared o' being in secht o' the castle.' This was Neil and Donald's theory for such a harvest of pearls remaining in shallow, easily fished waters.

We were just about to start another run when Davy hissed: 'Weesht! Bide where ye are. Someone's watching us fae the road.'

Peering through the trees, I saw the blue-and-cream livery of a landrover positioned so as to view the water in front of the castle. It moved off after a minute but we decided to fish on. If we were to be chased, we didn't intend to leave anything, and we added a few more to the bottle before climbing back to the road. Donald and Neil had got nothing. Years later, Neil told me that they'd just sat in the car while we did their dirty work. It was still quite early, but we'd had a good day and with sixty miles of winding road between us and home, we took off our waders and had a leisurely drive back.

My share was £13: a week's money for an afternoon's pleasure, exploring new country in the company of men for whom the land and its history were inextricably entwined with their own lives.

Later we fished down river opposite Fortingall, but well away from the road up the glen, and 'The Dool' came with us. The Dool was typical of a group of odd, rootless people who abound in the Blairgowrie area. Some come to pick berries or to do other casual work which may be found on the farms in winter. Nobody knew his origins, though rumour had it that he'd been a seaman. He went by the name Willy, but I never heard a surname mentioned. Donald dubbed him 'The Dool' because he had 'Dool's feet', and only Donald knew what they were. He was broke most of the time and hung round Yeaman Street waiting for us to go to the shells. He tagged along, and although he didn't fish or contribute to petrol costs, he got a share of the food, cigarettes from Donald and Neil and perhaps a few pints of beer, and saw a great deal of the country. However, this was not enough.

One day he tried fishing without waders and nearly died of cold, but the pearl-fishers' free-spending ways drew him like a magnet so he asked Wee Andy if he could borrow his waders. Andy hadn't been fishing much since starting work on the oil pipeline and handed them over, saying: 'They're no bad, but they need a bit o' sortin'[1] roond the gowels.'[2] This was actually a bit of an understatement.

Neil and I fished away from the bank in a deep pool, and Donald went upstream. The Dool stuck by us but never left the shallows, not seeming to want to go above the 'gowels'.

Neil nudged me with a grin. 'The Dool's shudderin' wi' the cauld. He's either shipped o'er the top, or those awfy waders o' Andy's are lettin' in something terrible.'

Feigning lack of interest, we both watched covertly. The Dool was obviously suffering. He started for the bank, water pouring back into the river from holes he hadn't even suspected. The enormous weight of water inside the waders made itself felt, the more he emerged from the river. From the back, with legs like two blubbering, creased bags of jelly, he looked like an old bull elephant struggling out of a waterhole. Reaching the bank, instead of taking the waders down and emptying them, he lay on his back and raised his legs in the air. The water, which had only been up to his crotch, rushed out and washed up his chest and down his back, making him gasp.

Donald arrived and almost fell on his knees laughing. 'Ye'd be better wi' nae waders, min!'

'I'll keep them on,' muttered Willy wryly. 'The water inside heats up after a while.'

'Ye're tryin' tae heat the 'hale river,' Donald spluttered. 'It's gaein' in ane side an' oot the other.'

Apart from one more day at the Tummel, when the Dool and I made ourselves sick drinking water from below the Pitlochry sewage farm, he abandoned his attempt to make a fortune from pearls but often came for the ride.

A spell of pleasant weather and low water heralded summer. We were drawn to the rivers every day. At weekends, as many as seven of us crammed into Neil and Donald's white Austin Cambridge. One such evening, returning from an afternoon at the Tay, where we had been without waders, we were leaving the A9 at Dunkeld,

[1] Mending.
[2] Crotch, male parts.

turning onto the Blairgowrie road, when the car keeled right over and, with a great CRACK, stayed on its beam end like a stricken ship with a shifted cargo. The nearside leaf spring was snapped right through. Luckily its broken ends were embedded in the chassis, and the car couldn't drop any further.

'We should hae ta'en the van springs off Noddy,' lamented Donald. To withstand severe road conditions and too many passengers, they'd put one-ton van springs on the old Wolseley. This raised the rear of the car so much that its front shock-absorbers gave way, and it got its nickname from the nodding motion after it hit a bump. Typically there was little real concern for the car. The seven of us just got back in and drove the twelve miles to Blair.

The following day we went to the scrapyard for springs. At each end stood a grimy caravan. The smaller one had its door hanging off to reveal an indescribably filthy interior. It was occupied by a cocky little Irishman whom Donald called 'The Bowery'. He was about five foot two, with a mane of jet black hair, a blue chin and jackdaw's eyes. His own circumstances were of no consequence to him. As long as he had the price of a pint and some tobacco, all was well with the world. I was puzzled how he was always unshaven to the same degree whenever we met him. He probably used a razor mounted on rollers that kept it an eighth of an inch above his skin.

The other caravan was occupied by 'The Count's' family. The Count was a long, slightly stooped man whose age was disguised by the oily grime of his trade. Donald's nicknames were always accurate caricatures, and this was no exception. The resemblance to Dracula was so strong that I had to turn away to regain control. His wife had the straight, middle-parted black hair and high cheekbones of a Red Indian squaw and had lost all her teeth. These people were of Irish origin but were distantly related to Donald through his Stewart cousins. They and the Stewarts had fished for pearls during the 1950s and sixties, when a good day's fishing could buy a pick-up truck for scrap collection, or a reasonable car.

While we stripped the springs, their small boy, a pasty-faced bag of bones with a hacking cough, perched on the wreck like a monkey. Taking the last cigarette from a twenty packet, he threw the packet away, took out a fresh packet and offered it round with casual assurance of one smoking man among others. He told us in a matter of fact way that he'd been in hospital with TB the previous year, and smoked forty cigarettes a day. Donald wasn't impressed with all this. 'Where d'ye get the money?' he gasped in amazement.

'Och, I steal it fae them,' he gestured towards the caravan.

'How old are ye?' Neil asked.

'Nine.'

By nightfall we had extra leaves built into both my car and Donald and Neil's. Instead of trailing their rear ends like hyenas, they had a purposeful crouch.

When we fished 'abin the toon', as anywhere above Grantown-on-Spey was called, we usually used the A9 as it crosses the upper part of the Spey. On one occasion, Donald, Neil, Gordon and I, accompanied by the ubiquitous Dool, fished up from the old cemetery pool. The Dool was along for the ride and was penniless as usual. Due to the scarcity of shells 'abin the toon', we walked miles to fish short stretches between long blanks. Despite the scarcity, crooks sat in plain view. We must have been the first to fish that part that season, and I believe that, being left over winter, some crooks that had been hidden for perhaps thirty years must have moved out of cover. By evening we had a good bottle of pearls and walked contentedly back to the car through the open birch woods above the riverside.

9. The Auld Road and Allargue

When the snow had left the hills, we fished the Spey more often. The 'auld road' was the shorter of the two routes we could take to the river but was hard on cars and took just as long as the A9. Saving petrol was more important than saving cars.

The 'auld road', to us, was the road to the Spey by Glenshee and Braemar, then over the Lecht to Tomintoul. That it was made up of two or three separate roads, depending on where we were fishing, was of no matter. It was all one to us. It begins as the A93 Braemar road, climbing out of Rattray by a steep, wooded cleft below Craighall Gorge, then enters Glenshee. It is easy to justify the words of an old song whose refrain is, 'I'll ta'k ye tae Glenisla, by bonny Glenshee.' Within the glen, framed by the distant hills, a rolling road wanders a landscape of small hills, forest, rocky fields, farmland and heather moor. Each turn and rise brings new aspects. Nearer the head of the glen, the hills on either side close in. The road here once climbed steeply through a series of hairpin bends at the notorious 'Devil's Elbow', now straightened for ski traffic. It then drops into a lonely glen whose waters enter the Dee at Braemar.

Beyond Braemar, the Dee valley is heavily forested for several miles. Huge old Scots pines stand in an undergrowth of thick heather along the course of the rocky river. Above them, the newer forests of larch and spruce grow to the foot of rocky outcrops overhanging parts of the valley. Most of the nine miles from Braemar to our turning, and beyond, pass through land either owned by the Farquharsons of Invercauld, whose castle can be seen to the north of the river, or in the Queen's Balmoral Estate on the south bank.

Opposite Balmoral, a tiny road turns up the hill to the north. It was all single track in those days and still bears an undeserved A-road status. Its steepness, hairpin bends and hump-backed bridges deterred touring coaches from using that route. At one point, just north of Cock Bridge and the River Don, the road rises to two thousand feet in a series of zigzags. This part, known as 'The Lecht', is so frequently and deeply blocked by snow that Alpine snow-blowers struggle to keep it clear.

The Allargue Arms at Cock Bridge is the natural stopping-place for us on the way home from the Spey, or anywhere to the north. It stands on a grassy slope above the infant River Don, right at the foot of the Lecht. We always had to 'let the brakes cool' after descending the hill. Allargue (pronounced A-largee), known as 'Briggies' by the locals from the two bridges and as 'the pearl-fishers' downfall' by our wives, became our local, despite being nearly sixty miles from home.

From Allargue to Speyside is about twenty-five miles, in which there is only one garage, at Tomintoul. It is the only garage in nearly fifty miles between Braemar and Grantown-on-Spey. After the great, rounded, heather-covered hills along the Lecht, the land falls away to a broad country of high moorland and spruce plantations near Tomintoul. Fields clawed from the moorland produce grass, oats and turnips.

Beyond Tomintoul and the wild River Avon (pronounced 'Arn'), the high moor continues, cut by the occasional deep glen, as at Bridge of Brown. Further on, a huge tract of partially reclaimed moorland sprawls westward to the foot of a massive range of snow-capped hills. These hills, the Cairngorms, look down on the Spey Valley which forms a green strip below the dark forests and hills of the northern skyline. From this viewpoint, the road falls in a series of undulations till, at the bottom of the last hill, the river can be seen through a screen of birches.

The lack of garages, the sort of cars we used, the nature of the road, and drink made the eighty miles or so to the Spey something of a risk. The drive took nearly three hours and was the prelude to the sort of day that those who buy the jewellery, and men whose wives say: 'Had a hard day at the office, dear?' cannot possibly conceive. It usually comprised six hours' driving, seven hours' pearl-fishing and five hours' drinking.

The driving was on roads that gave no room for error: the

fishing meant walking several miles, much of it bent double against a strong current of freezing water, and stumbling over slippery boulders carrying a heavy bag of shells, for seven hours without food or drink. As for the drinking ... Most people have their stories, some may even imagine they know something of drink, but unless they'd been with the pearl-fishers, I'd be inclined to discount it as idle boasting. For most men, to brag of their ability to take drink and stay on their feet would be enough, but to take what these men took, then walk or work everyone else off theirs, was unbelievable. I think pearl-fishing in summer and winter piece-work in the local raspberry field seasoned them to endure almost anything.

Allargue had become something of an institution among the pearl-fishers, and they were similarly regarded as customers. The long road to the Spey became so much a part of my life that summer, and the summers of the following nine years. The sing-song Aberdeenshire dialect grew steadily more intelligible through frequent stops at Allargue, and it would be no boast to say that I knew more people in that area than I do in Camberley, my home for twelve years.

Licensing laws were interpreted differently in the hills. I once heard of a policeman looking in at eleven-thirty, though, not being present, it could just be gossip. As it was an hour and a half after closing time in those days, there could have been trouble. However, Archie Stewart merely asked the alleged policeman if he wanted a dram, but he was on his way to Tomintoul and hadn't time to stop.

If we stopped for a drink on the way *up* to the Spey at half past eight or nine o'clock in the morning, we went into the tiny bar and called through to the kitchen. If Archie was out at his sheep, his wife or 'Young Archie' would come through and serve us.

Allargue was the social centre of the head of Strathdon, the haunt of gamekeepers, deerstalkers, hill farmers and shepherds. In winter it is now the haunt of skiers. The solitary bar used to be about twelve feet square. It had three bar stools and two hardboard benches along the sides. The men's toilet opened directly off it. Ladies were not catered for. On stormy nights they had to go through the bar hatch to the kitchen, then into the lobby to reach a toilet, or brave the elements in a mad dash round to the front door in darkness.

Whenever we arrived and had got our first round of drinks, Archie would ask if we'd done well that day and call Mary through to see the pearls. They were emptied into a clean ashtray and shown round. Mary would then ask: 'Drappy soupy, boys?' This was old-fashioned Highland hospitality, extended to the pearl-fishers as opposed to 'mere customers', who were taken by surprise when they had to pay for theirs. It didn't matter if there were eight of us; steaming bowls of home-made broth appeared with unfailing regularity, and the hospitality didn't end there. Before being allowed to face sixty miles of unlit mountain road after a fierce night's drinking, we were often led through to the kitchen and given coffee, and oatcakes and scones baked on the peat-fired Rayburn.

In the early days, few tourists used the bar at night. Those that did often listened in uncomprehending silence to the alien tongues of their fellow inmates. Many, even some Scots, would have been as well in a Greek *taverna* for all they understood of the conversation. The dialect was severely modified for visitors from England, or further afield. Nevertheless, they enjoyed it as local colour.

Tourists liked talking to the pearl-fishers. A night with them was something special in their holiday, something that couldn't be photographed or bought in a gift shop. Only memory can do justice to such things. Half drunk, with interest awakened, they came to life, unconsciously creating a store of memories to be taken out in similar circumstances or on quiet evenings in years to come. The tiny bar was part of an almost mythological Scotland they had been searching for. It couldn't be packaged for general consumption without devaluing it but had to be stumbled on. Many times I saw the pleasure of discovery on the rapt faces of listeners whose intense interest became almost an embarrassment.

I feel it necessary to say in our defence that, although a lot of money from the pearls has been invested in Allargue, it has done some good. The bar has been enlarged, though, of course, the atmosphere has gone with the old one, and tourists are in the majority in the skiing season. We don't pretend to be entirely responsible for funding these developments, but I'm sure Archie would be first to acknowledge a significant contribution.

On the night of the Lonach Games in Strathdon, or if the Stewarts were at a wedding or suchlike, all their family and most of the regulars would be there too. One of our number would duck under the bar hatch and take over. By the end of the evening he was leaning on the bar between pulling pints, chatting amiably to customers as if he owned the place, and Donald called him 'The Highland Hotelier' for the rest of the season.

10. Speysiders

While local rivers still produced enough pearls for a good living, Donald and Neil didn't have to drive the eighty miles to the Spey from necessity. Even the pearl-fisher, whose workplace would be a different part of Glen Lyon or Strathtay every day, likes a change. A change of river adds a little excitement, and a new one raises it to fever pitch.

As the Tay and its tributaries, the Aberdeenshire rivers, the Forth and the South Esk all became played out, we fished the Spey more frequently. Trips to rivers even further afield became a necessity too. We thought nothing of fishing a river in the north of England, going for a drink, then deciding at closing time to drive through the night to fish the Conway in the morning.

Eventually the River Spey became our bread-and-butter river and replaced the Tay, which, being nearer to the urban central lowlands, was prey to weekend pearlers and divers.

From its source near Loch Spey in the Monadhliath Mountains, the River Spey flows east to meet the River Truim near the A9, then turns slightly, heading north-east down its broad valley, entering the sea at Spey Bay just east of the Moray Firth. The mussel beds of the River Spey once covered nearly half its 107-mile length. Since the early 1970s the upper twenty miles have been fished out and, though the lower ten miles miles of mussel bed are well stocked, it is only because you'd need to kill a couple of thousand or more to get a pearl. We've tried! The dearth of pearls might be caused by a tributary, the Avon, which runs through a belt of limestone by Tomintoul. Below its confluence with the Spey, the shells don't even look the same, and pearls are suddenly rare.

Even the 'guid bit' has 'nae use' bits in the middle of it. Of the twenty miles of Spey in which we spent much of our time, quite a lot was either a 'soup dungeon', as Donald called the silted deeps, or a 'rattle o' boulders', which were boulder-strewn rapids. The Spey is the fastest-flowing river in Britain, and rapids and 'heavy streams' were frequent barriers to fishing. Quieter water, even at the side of these stretches, often produced pearls, though the good bottom seldom stretched across the river as it does in some parts of the Tay. From these restricted areas of one part of the river, my friends and I alone have taken tens of thousands of pounds' worth of pearls over the years, and a good few thousand from the rest. Lord knows what the total would be if all the other fishers were taken into account. Despite this, the *Encyclopaedia of World Rivers* refers to the fine salmon-fishing of the Tay and Spey and the latter's distilleries but makes no mention of pearls.

The speed of the Spey has been the salvation of its pearl mussels. Even in very heavy streams, as we call the rapids, where there is shelter from firmly bedded rocks and sand may still collect, shells fill every square inch of it. The shallower streams are fished out, particularly near the bank, but some streams are both deep and swift. The only way they are likely to be eradicated is by pollution, and this is unlikely in a river on which powerful salmon-fishing and whisky industries depend. These heavy streams were also largely ignored by professional pearl-fishers because they were relatively unproductive. The new breed of weekend pearlers had no inherited knowledge of the river and just killed shells where they found them, so they have few safe places now. Only where the water is too fierce, even when the river is very low, can they be assured of surviving.

Heavy streams are exhausting places to fish. Forward motion is akin to walking on ice cubes into a hurricane. Bent double over the jug, face close to the surface, the noise fills your head like an express train in a tunnel, and the water races beneath so wildly you feel as if you're looking through the hull of a glass-bottomed speed-boat. The effort of holding the jug racks the muscles, and the tangs are held clear of the water for this reason, and to allow two hands to be used to guide the jug. The wake the jug makes causes bubbles to travel under the glass and confuse the eye, or else it sweeps over it and almost snatches it from your grasp. If you are lucky enough to be able to stand in one place long enough to see shells through this maelstrom, the second the tangs enter the water, they weigh a hundredweight and develop palsy. It is at this point that the jug strikes a 'lump' of water rising over a rock and bucks, cracking your brow or bursting your lip on your teeth. You raise your tangs, and the shell you fought for is washed out of the mouth and lands about twenty-five yards behind you. The feeling of relief when you reach quiet water is marvellous.

Most of our fishing was done below Grantown-on-Spey, or 'The Toon', as it was called. Further upstream was known simply as 'abin the toon' and involved a lot more walking to find shells, especially if there were four or five of us. When shells were scarce, we covered ground more rapidly. Where the good bottom was wide enough, two people worked a strip, each zigzagging to cover as much bottom as possible. Another pair would have entered the water thirty or forty yards upstream, perhaps calling down to describe a tree or rock that could be used as a mark that would prevent the same bit being fished twice. Four men fishing singly, some skimping to get on to a better bit, can soon devour several miles of river, leapfrogging this way.

We were far from being alone in fishing the Spey. The Williamsons from Inverness, the MacMillans from Elgin, the Davises of Dornoch and several other families of pearl-fishers and travellers could be encountered. The MacMillans didn't seem to fish any other river. They lived in bow camps beside the river during the summer months.

These camps sometimes congregate into little villages of half a dozen fishers' shelters, usually out of sight among trees, or on an island if they're near the road. Each bow camp is made by cutting ash or hazel saplings and pushing their ends into the ground to form two parallel rows enclosing the living-space. The tops are bent over to meet in an inverted 'U' and bound together. A 'keel' piece is interwoven along the top, and cross pieces are woven into the sides for rigidity. With a canvas cover, the finished camp looks like an upside-down barge.

The small, one-man camps by the river were often covered with a patchwork of polythene fertilizer sacks and carpeted with a bale of straw scattered around the earth floor. One of the MacMillans had an old dresser top with drawers in it containing his tea, sugar and milk, standing near his fire. The travellers would always drink tea, never using the unboiled river for drinking. They might take water from small burns but, more often than not, went to houses to have their kettles filled. This gave them the chance of getting some milk or a bite of 'meat' at the same time.

Near Stanley, between Perth and Blairgowrie, a back road that passes near the Tay often has a couple of camps by it. They are what Donald would call 'executive bows' and are perhaps fifteen feet long. A family of six or seven might be brought up in a camp like this, suffering all weathers. These 'family' camps have a stove for cooking and heating. The pipe passes through a piece of sheet metal to prevent its coming into contact with the canvas and keep the rain out.

The regular pearl-fishing camps were given names, the most common of which is probably 'The Lucky Camp'. A camp by the Keithick Stream, as we call a shallow, rushy stretch of the Isla, bears this name. Another I have heard tell of was at Rosehall on the River Oykell. There is no luck to be had at either of these places now.

The travelling people of Scotland are a different race from the English Romanies. The Romanies originated in the mountains of north-west India and Afghanistan, beginning their migration westwards only about eight hundred years ago. Their language bears witness to this. Until just before World War II they crossed back and forth over the frontiers of most European countries at will. They called themselves 'Rom', which means in their language simply 'man'. Those who came to Britain are now a mixed race who speak a dialect which contains many words from the language of the Rom. This has become mixed with the dialect of Scottish travellers, though its influence in Scotland is strongest in the south.

The Scottish travellers are Highlanders who were long settled in their own lands when the Rom began their migration. They are the descendants of the hapless survivors of Culloden, their families and other Jacobite sympathizers, real or imagined. They were dispossessed, hunted, humiliated and broken. The survivors took to the road, marked by their way of life as rebels and forced to beg from those they despised as supporters of the English, or who had sat on the fence. Even many of their own kind who had escaped the wrath of the English and their quislings persecuted or, at the least, shunned them. The number of travellers was probably swollen by victims of the Highland clearances who could not afford a passage to the New World. The tinkling of pots and kettles on their passing carts gave them the name tinklers, then tinkers, and now the derisive 'tink'. In this despised sub-culture, the ways and language of the Highlanders survived, while the rest of the populace were Anglicized, further serving to isolate them.

The remains of this language are still in common use today. The travellers call it 'Cant'. Its framework is English, but many of its words are Gaelic, or derivatives of it; some are Old Scots, the language of government and the south-eastern lowland people; a few of the words come from the Romanies, and there are even some that are echoes of 'the Auld Alliance' with France. There are interesting stories behind many of these words. The Scots plural of 'e'e' ('eye' pronounced 'ee') is 'e'en'. The travellers might use the singular in the same way but often say 'yax' in the plural, which is so close to the French '*yeux*'. Another link is the word 'loor', meaning money. Neil and Mary McCormick told me this derived from a French coin, and in *Rob Roy* I remember reading of the '*louis d'or*'.

One of the most fascinating survivals is the word for 'shame', which is pronounced 'shahn', from a Gaelic spelling of *Seann*. Donald's McGregor ancestors were such a troublesome clan that they were outlawed and proscribed. They took the names of friendly neighbours or powerful allies and, when their tartan was banned, wore trousers or trews. There is a Highland dance still performed today called '*Seann Triubhas*',* meaning 'Shameful Trews'. Its movements symbolize the casting off of the trousers which were an anathema to a proud people.

One night we were returning from the Spey, via Allargue, and stopped to show our pearls to a traveller and his son who camped at the side of a burn just across the Dee from Balmoral Castle. The tents were visible in the glare of a big fire under the trees across the burn, but nobody answered Donald's cry of: 'Aye, ged!' We drove on and shared the bottle of beer we had brought for them. A couple of days later we saw the man as we were on our way up to the Spey, and stopped to speak. Donald told him we'd not seen

* Pronounced 'Shiarn trews'.

anyone in the camp and had shouted to no avail.

'I didnae ken it was you boys,' the traveller replied. 'I thocht it was the *seann hantle*.'

When we got out of earshot, Donald began to laugh.' The *seann hantle*, ged! They'll hae lain in their tent keekin'* oot, thinkin' the redcoats were coming, or folk fae the village come tae beat them up and ravish the women.'

This was a relic of the days when travellers' camps must have been targets for local thugs, who would no doubt arrive in superior numbers and do as they pleased with the women, beating anyone who got in their way. *Seann hantle* obviously were folk, or at least men, who shamed the travellers.

For people in their position, pearl-fishing was an ideal profession. It could be carried on in remote places, pearls would be sold on rare visits to towns, and it broke no laws. I have heard stories of dealers buying pearls at the waterside, but as often as not fine pearls were taken to the back door of the nearest 'big hoose', and smaller ones bartered for food at farms.

Donald's uncle, the late Alec Stewart, or 'Auld Eck', as he was known, once told us about the bartering. He was Andra Stewart's older brother and a famous piper known for his fund of old tunes. Andra himself was a piper and storyteller, and articles and booklets have been published about the family by Edinburgh University. Auld Eck's wife, Bell, is a folksinger, and together they have been invited to folk festivals all over the world, as well as appearing on television and radio frequently. They were also pearl-fishers.

We'd been away for a couple of days and come back with a good weight of pearls in the bottle, though nothing of special quality. Donald took them along the road to show Eck. Despite the weight and number of pearls, Auld Eck was not impressed and commented: 'Och, they're no bad, but they're sugar an' tea pearls.'

Donald asked him what he meant.

'We used tae geng tae a fermhoose door wi' the like o' that and swap them for sugar and tea.'

Auld Eck would most likely be talking about the 1930s, when pearls were plentiful and in vogue, a rare combination of

* Looking, peering.

advantages to fishers. War brought fishing to a virtual halt, and it wasn't till the early 1950s that it picked up again. It was in the late fifties that Donald, then Neil, began to fish. Neil and Mary were talking about those days, a year or two before they were married, and of times when the whole McGregor family would hitch up caravans to lorries, pick-ups and cars and set off wherever the fancy took them. Mary and Donald's father, Andy, and his brother Donald, their wives and children, some married, and even some nephews and cousins, would form a great convoy. Many of the men dealt in scrap metal, cars, lorries and caravans and could raise the convoy from their 'stock'.

Neil and Donald worked together for Andy McGregor, and Neil was going out with Mary, one of eight daughters in the household. When they were leaving, he stood disconsolately on a corner to wave as they set off towards the hills and the west coast, or maybe even the islands. Andy must have felt for Neil when he saw him. He pulled up, bringing the whole line to a halt, and asked if he wanted to come. Neil didn't need to be asked twice. In minutes he had run home, packed a few clothes, said goodbye to his grandmother and was back at the corner.

Andy and Donald knew a lot of rivers along their way where they could pick up a few pearls, maybe even enough to cover the cost of the trip, or better. Neil must have felt as I did when I met Donald and him, and it was inevitable that, when he married Mary, the free and easy ways of his in-laws, that had already beckoned, should take full possession of him. It was also inevitable that his family would inherit knowledge of rivers, pearl-fishing lore and language that Donald in particular has elaborated into a slang cult.

It was remarkable that any of this has survived. In the centuries before Mikimoto produced the first 'true' cultured pearls at the end of the nineteenth century, it was not surprising that the oriental pearls, which must have been expensive, had failed to oust river pearls from popularity. The 'local' pearls would have been very much cheaper, yet dear enough to make pearl-fishing a lucrative profession when they were fashionable. The advent of cultured pearls reversed the price structure, yet freshwater pearls continued to be popular enough to provide a few pearling families with a livelihood, as well as a lot of travellers in other trades with a part-time income.

It is doubtful if any spate of pearl-fishing has ever matched the 'Pearl Fever' of the early 1860s. The phrase 'Pearl Fever' appeared in an *Illustrated London News* of the period which described the rush to the rivers. According to this report, a certain Moritz Unger of Edinburgh (the Cairncross Brothers, to whom we sell our pearls, tell me he was a German) started the rush by advertising that he would buy freshwater pearls found within easy reach of the capital. The Forth itself and its tributaries the Allan Water, the Devon, the Teith and its tributary the Balvaig, were all pearl rivers. News probably spread rapidly north to the huge Tay fishery which covered the whole Tay, the western end of Loch Tay, the Earn, the Lyon, the Dochart, the Lochay and the Tay's main tributary, the Tummel. The Tummel is nearly as long as the Tay, starting only about fourteen miles from the west coast and containing, in its upper reaches, the highest mussel beds we have come across in Britain.

The article describes a scene of almost gold-rush proportions: farm workers, labourers, school children and their teachers, and 'scantily clad ladies' wading the shallows. Every spare moment was spent looking for a find that could fetch more than a year's wages for some of them. There was even a blind woman who was led to the river, where she paddled in the shallows, feeling for the mussels with her feet. She apparently accumulated more money in a few weeks of low water than most men could earn in twelve months. This has all the hallmarks of the typical pearl-fishing tale, but, given that mussels were much more abundant in the shallows then, and the fact that fishers of ancient times groped blindly for them, it is not beyond the bounds of possibility.

Professional fishers no doubt operated all through this bonanza, strange, often secretive characters with names like 'Pearl Johnny' of Coupar Angus, 'Newburgh Jock' and the mysterious, fur-coated man who bought pearls at the riverside, of whom we heard from old-time fishers. Families of pearlers lived in each district, though some travelled extensively, and many were travelling people anyway.

The report speculated that there were possibly hundreds of other rivers in Scotland that might contain pearls. Many other rivers were already known, but the reports were not of sufficient depth to reveal them, or the fishers were 'ca'ing canny'! It is fairly certain that the poorer working people, for whom the boom in pearls was such a bounty, would know little outside their immediate area and would stick to local rivers. Travel in the Highlands was still a difficult undertaking.

Apart from the wealthy tourist, one other group had no such limitation on their knowledge of the country: the travellers. In their slow wandering over the old drovers' roads, through the empty glens and the quiet byways, two centuries of punishment for taking the wrong side, they took whatever they could from the land and the water and from those who had taken sides against them, the anglicized *seann hantle* who held *their* land and *their* homes. The names of pearl rivers and the best places on those rivers were handed down in families, often remaining virtually unknown outside the travelling fraternity.

Women and children fished alongside the men, barelegged in the freezing waters. I have seen a whole family of MacPhees fishing a 'pearl stream' in the Spey in this manner. Three generations were there. Mother, father and five children were in the water, and the grandfather and grandmother sat on the bank watching the kettle on the fire.

In this way the children learned things only experience could teach: how to read the water and bottom, and the indefinable ability to pick out a crook among hundreds of half-buried mussels in several feet of peaty water. These were the skills which it would take me several more years of concentrated fishing to master, despite the primitive tools and the ease of mimicking the actions of pearl-fishing so that you look like a professional at the end of the first week. The travellers' children also bypassed the expensive trial and error that amateurs go through before they discover that not all rivers contain mussels, that not all rivers that contain mussels are populated by pearl mussels, and that, even if they are, they might not produce sufficient pearls to make them pay. Add to that the miles of mussel beds in good rivers where a man can be driven to despair, as I almost was in the Spey, lifting bag after bag to no avail, and you have a virtual 'closed shop'. Without the help of a professional fisher today, it would be impossible to make a profit on a season of pearl-fishing.

The travellers have strange views on some of the present-day aspects of their profession. For example, the shortage of mussels is not caused by overfishing, they say.

One evening, on our way home from a lower reach of the Spey we stopped by 'The Metal Brig', on seeing pearl-fishers downstream. Below the metal bridge was the lowest of the low to us. It was a place where shells lay in tens of thousands, and crooks were one in a thousand, making pearls even less frequent. We weren't above fishing it now and then and, with a lot of skill, picking through the mind-boggling mass of straight shells, and a great deal of luck, had occasionally had a reasonable day. This time we dismissed it totally as a place to fish again. Five travellers whom we'd never seen at the Spey before had come up through a backwash which used to be a carpet of black shells. They'd left it bare. A mound of dead mussels lay nearly two feet deep all along the side of it, sticking out of the water in places. We could only gape for a while.

'Ye dinnae hae tae kill the shells, ye ken,' Donald tried to reason.

'Peter here hardly kills a shell at a'. He just prises them a wee bit,' Neil added. He'd killed a lot of shells in his time but was shocked by what he'd seen.

They didn't want to know.

'Shells are scarce in the Spey the noo,' the eldest man said by way of conversation.

'What d'you think's the cause?' I asked innocently.

'Plooshn, plooshn,' he answered with the certainty of total ignorance. 'A' these distilleries mak' an awfy plooshn, ye ken.'

Donald, Neil and I glanced hopelessly at each other and made for the car, shaking our heads.

'Plooshn! Plooshn! Plooshn! there's nae pollution here. The salmon fisheries board'd geng moich. The fishing's too big.' Donald was getting hot under the collar. 'A pure moicher, ged! Folk wouldnae pay a hundred pound a day tae fish a polluted burn.'

One of the criteria for a good burn was that shells were scarce. This meant that it had been sorely fished and is a good guide to there having been a high proportion of crooks and pearls per bag of shells at one time. This has been turned into a kind of prejudice in which any stretch of water that has plenty of mussels in it is no use for pearls. Donald was fishing a burn on Skye with his older cousin Andy Stewart, many years before I met him. Andy looked into the water and immediately bolted for the car, shouting to a puzzled Donald, 'Too thick! Too thick!' Donald naturally, at that time, thought plenty of shells was a good thing but had to follow his more experienced partner. Years later, the Davises told Neil and him about this same burn. When he and his cousin had been there it had hardly been touched, and it was a very good pearl river as they found when they finally went back to it.

The prejudice had taken a new slant. Many of the more ignorant travellers now regard the places on the river which had been left alone because there were so few pearls in them as being, I quote: 'in need o' a guid thinnin' oot'. By this means, they actually believe the incidence of pearls will be increased.

The travellers had a fear of drowning by using waders and seldom wore them, fishing only up to the top of the legs when the water was cold. When the water got any deeper, they used a boat. We were often told that a river had a lot of 'boating water' on it, and found no trouble covering it all with our breast-high waders. On one northern river for example, the Davises thought nothing of carrying their boat five or six miles over broken moorland rather than put on high waders, which they thought increased the risk of drowning.

The boats used by most of these pearlers hardly merited the name. They were little more than a wooden-framed canvas box and were so light that they could easily be carried by one man. When long distances were to be covered, they could be folded flat and hung beside the crossbar of a bicycle. From such simple craft they could lift shells from considerable depths. I have taken shells from seventeen feet of water in the big hole above the old railway bridge at Logierait on the Tay. Fishing from an old one-man dinghy which went down almost as fast as I blew it up, I used a fifteen-foot bamboo pole, and the full length of my arm, to raise half a dozen shells from a ridge of rock and sand in the middle of the even deeper water at each side. I used my usual wading jug and could see quite clearly into this depth. There were no more shells to be seen, and I got a nice little ball from one of them, despite the difficulty of getting the very buoyant bamboo down the depth. If it wandered off the vertical, it couldn't be prevented from swinging through ninety degrees to lie on the surface. It probably should have been weighted because, even when working directly beneath the dinghy, as soon as I released it, it made for the sky like a rocket.

To fish deep, dark pools, where shells were well hidden by algae or freshwater sponge growth, a long jug was sometimes used. Donald and Neil had one with thick glass held in with waterproof concrete. This gave it the strength to withstand pressure at about six feet, which was its length, and the weight to let it float level with the side of the boat. It could be used only in still water and where shells were fairly dense, as it was hardly the most manoeuvrable piece of equipment. Boat-fishing deep water with a long jug had to be well organized and worth the considerable effort involved. Any kind of boat-fishing was like a spell on the rack. Boats had to be lifted on and off cars and sometimes carried long distances. Without proper anchors and a ratcheted hand-winch to work the boat in a zigzag up toward the anchors, it was well nigh impossible in moving water. With a single anchor, the fisher swings on his line like a pendulum. If he tangs a shell slightly away from him, in a light boat, he pushes himself in the other direction and 'loses his place'.

The usual way to fish a stretch is to drift over it, checking for shells. As soon as you see any, you drop an anchor to the right of the upstream end of the bed, then drop a second anchor to the left. Having let out both lines till you reach the limit of the shells, or the lines, you can then begin fishing. Let out of the right-hand line and the boat swings in an arc on the left one to cover the bottom on that side; then, by pulling in the right, or should I say starboard line, the arc covers the bottom below the first anchor's position. A ratcheted hand-winch for each line makes this a simple, systematic business, though lifting shells in deep, moving water is still extremely hard on the neck and shoulders. I find it an excellent means of stimulating migraine.

11. Lore and Language

Pearl-fishing is such a simple occupation, even to a beginner, that it is easy to imagine from a state of ignorance that anyone knowing some rivers with pearls in them and possessing the requisite limbs and eyes, can almost immediately perform as well as anyone else. After all, you need only a glass and a stick, then it's just a matter of walking into the water, looking for shells and picking them up. If you don't think you can stand the cold water, a pair of waders and a bag to put the shells in will round off your air of expertise, which is belied only by a lack of pearls in your bottle.

I used to describe this by an analogy. Give someone who'd never played golf a set of rules, and a manual of the arts of the game, supply them with clubs and balls, then expect them to play off a handicap of five, once they'd read the books. However, if the analogy fitted pearl-fishing, the golfer would swing beautifully, use all the correct clubs and, with every appearance of skill, achieve nothing. The pearl-fisher's ability to pick out crooks is almost like a sixth sense. It is akin to the ability of some people to predict the turning of a playing card significantly more often than by pure guesswork. Take a newcomer to pearl-fishing, equip him properly and set him right beside you to fish, and he might just get a bigger pearl or even a greater number than you, just as the golf 'rabbit' might tee off to a hole in one. At the end of a year he will be a better fisher but will still be finding it hard to understand why you can make a living while he has the occasional good day and you have the odd poor one.

Beginners tend to stand on the spot where mussels are fairly plentiful and try to lift everything. Finding shells left by the more experienced fishers, they think they are missing them. In fact, they are rejecting them. A few mussels always get passed over, even a crook or two, but no matter how fast or slow the professional moves, he gets more pearls. If he races upriver, he covers more ground, sees more crooks and takes more pearls. If he takes his time, poking under weeds, looking behind rocks, he gets more of what there is in that place and leaves what is ahead of him for another day.

A pearl-fisher must be sure of what he is looking for and, just as important, be quickly aware when it is absent. Going to a new river or a different area sorts the men from the boys. There is a fine balance between giving up too soon and going on too long, which has, like other aspects of the job, a little luck involved. Though we often appeared to skimp in the early days, my colleagues knew that time wasted looking for what was not readily available could have been spent filling the bottle. What they put in the bottle made the point abundantly clear to me, and what we have learned recently of places we skipped over in previous years shows fairly few mistakes were made. It took me several years of full-time fishing to reach this degree of proficiency. The fact is demonstrated by my ability to find more shells and more pearls now in places I'd once struggled to make anything of.

It was now midsummer 1973, and I had been pearl-fishing for about two years, though only approximately three months of this had been of the intensive kind of learning, under the guidance of my friends, that I needed. I could make more of a contribution to the bottle of pearls than previously, and didn't have to say 'What?' or 'Pardon?' every time someone spoke. I began to learn, and use, the stock of highly descriptive terms of my new trade. Many of these were common to other Perthshire fishers, though some were local corruptions of them, and the remainder seemed to be inventions of Donald's, which, like so many of his creations, gained more meaning than the originals. Neil, too, used some old Scots words that I'd never heard elsewhere.

The most comprehensive aspect of pearling jargon is that describing the variety of shells, closely followed by terms describing river bottoms. The rivers themselves exert a powerful hold on pearl-fishers. The mere sight of one excites their interests so much that any other topic of conversation is dropped till it has fallen behind the car. 'That's a barry burn, ged,' someone says, meaning that it's a good river. Anything from a little stream up to the St Lawrence River is a burn to us. If we were going to fish a burn, we naturally meant pearl-fish. To avoid confusion, any other kind of fishing was properly announced. For example, Donald would say that he was fishing 'for troots', or whatever. If anyone met us on the way to the river and asked what we were doing, we were never 'going pearl-fishing'. The answer was, 'We're gaein' tae the shells.'

I had been puzzled by the names of some of the equipment we used: 'jug' didn't seem to bear any relation to its function till Neil told me that many of the travellers used to use a four-pint enamel milk jug with a glass bottom sealed with candle wax. We often find these, and 'National' baby milk tins, lying in the river. The milk jug at least had a handle. The really impoverished fishers use a pane of glass held on the surface. In reasonably smooth water it gives a horizontal strip about an inch and a half deep through which the bottom can be seen.

'Tangs' is Scots for 'tongs', hence the plural 'set of tangs' applied to one stick. The cleft pole that we use is thousands of years old but was superseded for a while by a pole with two iron spoons tied face to face at one end.

That summer I bought my first pair of seamless waders. Now I was shot of the appalling 'easy waders', the soft rubber feet of the new waders required 'wading boots' to protect them from sharp stones and broken bottles in the water and from barbed wire on the bank. Wading boots were improvised from worn lace-up boots or cut-down wellingtons. If they were forgotten, I've seen Neil and Donald cut open their good shoes to squeeze their waders in. In those days a pair of shoes, even good ones, were nothing to a day's fishing.

Occasionally a piece of barbed wire lying near an old fence would spring up like a cobra striking and hole the waders so that they 'let in'. Bending in the sun and flexing the knees, the back and knees of the waders became porous with age and let in. The crotch was also a weak spot. A hole there was announced by the remark, 'I'm shipping at the gowels' (genitals in Scots slang). 'Shipping' also meant going over the top of the waders in deep water. With confidence born of practice, we often fished to within a hair's breadth of the top of the waders. A little slack fold in the top sometimes hung down before you reached full depth, and a pint of freezing water had got in before you noticed, taking its time to soak into your clothes before it got to the skin. Donald called it a 'pook' or, more usually, 'a dirty pook', because it was sneaky.

'Bottoms' had long been a mystery to me. I'd learned fairly quickly what kind of bottom shells liked, but it had little to do with whether pearls would be found or not. As a beginner, I was tempted, naturally, to where there were plenty of shells. This seemed to be away from the bank where the water was a little quicker and where there was less weed to hide them. Filling the bag was easy on the 'bright bottom', as Neil called the coarse yellow sand and reddish shells that covered it. He preferred a 'technicolour bottom', especially if there was 'grumption' on it.

Near the side, there was often a strip of good bottom in which sand of a finer grade collected in the slower current. Weeds flourished. They were not the long, dense masses of Fontinalis found on the bright bottom, but little flickering tufts, mixed with pale green, red and almost white, fern-like weeds that clung to black rocks between which the sand collected. The 'grumption' looked to me like a freshwater sponge. It was an almost fluorescent pale green, like a reflective armband, and covered the rocks in patches. It even covered the shells where they were jammed between stones for any length of time. Neil's 'technicolour' bottom was a veritable aquatic garden. One such place on the Spey produced so many pearls for Andra Stewart that it bears his nickname 'Pandora's Stream' among us. All that remains there now is weed, stone and water.

In general, the geology and topography of a river decide its bottom by influencing water acidity, speed and depth. Fast water or hard rock produce a 'hard bottom', though such a bottom may appear poor because the layer of sand the young mussels hide in is merely concealed beneath stones. Some parts of the Spey are like this and are still well-known pearl streams. Even though easily fished, being shallow and near the bank, young mussels continually rise up through the stones to replace those taken.

Donald frequently referred to a 'metal' bottom, which I took to be one of his exaggerated descriptions of a very hard bottom. My guess wasn't far out, as he actually meant the 'metal' used to bed railway sleepers. The almost extinct Laxford in Sutherland has a 'metal' bottom, virtually the entire river being composed of angular gravel, with intermittent tumbles of jagged boulder or coarse, gravelly sand, yet it was a great pearl river. All our theorizing never got past the stage of being a generalization, and we constantly came on exceptions that made us eat our words. In the end, any bottom that 'threw' pearls was a good one, no matter what it looked like. This leads to another explanation. Burns 'throw' crooks, and crooks are supposed to throw pearls. This term seems widespread among pearlers.

After an opening, which I thought was at some arbitrary spot, Donald and Neil often ignored a large stretch of river and simply walked past it. My natural impulse was to fish on, but I was forgetting that they had fished almost every inch of most of the rivers we'd visited. When I asked why we weren't fishing that bit, the usual answer was a curt, 'Nae bottom.' At first I took it to be an exaggeration which meant bottomless, or at least too deep to fish. Finally I took a look. Usually there was shifting sand or gravel or a sheet of bare rock in these places, which was 'nae bottom' for shells to live on.

I was soon made aware of the value of 'backwashes'. There are two kinds of backwash, both of which are worth checking. The first occurs where a natural barrier, such as a rock or fallen tree, deflects the current away from the bank and creates a circular eddy in its lee. Near the bank, this eddy travels upstream, strikes the back of the obstruction and flows outwards to rejoin the main current. Shells containing growing pearls become gradually less able to bear the stronger current, (I believe) are dislodged and finish in the slower waters of the backwash.

The construction of stone barriers to create a fast current off its end where salmon will pass has caused artificial backwashes full of what Donald calls 'soup'. 'Soup' is a brown layer of decomposing organic matter, mainly rotting vegetation, that silts up the downstream side of these obstructions. What was once a healthy 'stream' can become a calm pool of warm, bacteria-laden water with an oxygen content that is too low for mussels to develop in. Only in winter, when high water stirs up the sediment, is it a suitable habitat for mussels. These man-made barriers are often too long to allow the reverse current to be of sufficient strength to keep the bottom clear of soup and frequently are placed so close together that long stretches of rivers are spoiled for mussels. Shells are then found only on the upstream side of the obstruction where the water begins moving again: a few yards out of a whole stretch they once occupied.

The second type of backwash is simply the lesser channel, or channels, where the river divides round one or more islands. The close proximity of the bank and the shallow bottom slows the current down and enables sickly crooks to maintain their hold. It was in this type of backwash in the River Dart that I found the first two pearl mussels I clapped eyes on.

At the river in Northumberland the previous year, Neil had told me he liked to see 'pool and stream, time aboot'. Though the terms were explained, they bear further comment. They appear in *Rob Roy*, where Rob escapes from captivity while crossing the River Forth's upper reaches, and were obviously colloquial terms for shallow rushes and deep, calm water at the turn of the seventeenth century. They remain part of our lore at the end of the twentieth century.

'Streams' are our general term for moving water that varies from rapids, which we call 'heavy streams', down to shallow, chattering little rushes near the bank. The water is well oxygenated, too quick for soup, yet not heavy enough to scour down to gravel. Where there is shade from the black alder trees that fringe the banks, weed growth can never choke the bottom and reduce the habitat available for mussels, which is commonplace where estates with valuable salmon fishing cut the trees to give as much access as possible from the bank without the danger of fishers foul hooking in branches. All hail Salmo, which can be bought in Blairgowrie as cheaply as mince.

Streams are the river's nursery. They are favoured by the trout which deposit the mature glochidia there in ideal conditions for their own survival, and for the formation of pearls. Unfortunately they are very easy to fish. Pearl-fishers 'read' the water, seeking out these places first, but a good fisher will hedge his bets by checking the poorer places too. 'Holes' and 'dungeons' have to be watched out for, though they are of less danger to pearl-fishers, who can see them through their jugs, than to salmon-fishers groping blindly out, prodding the bottom with sticks. Donald's graphic description 'dungeon' was usually reserved for the worst holes, which were deep and steep sided. They are difficult and dangerous to fish. The sides are often tumbled boulders from which it is very easy to slip while reaching down the slope for a shell. Surprisingly large rocks may tilt as soon as your weight falls on them, and slide into the darkness beneath.

Equally dangerous holes occur where the current scoops out sand or gravel from a stream, for no apparent reason. Their upstream lip often has shells that tempt the fisher onto an unstable surface of sloping shingle with his back to the current. Eddies caused by your feet can make the gravel wash away from round your boots and they lose their grip.

'Pools' usually occur at the top and bottom of streams. They are not necessarily deep but are generally calm stretches. The deeper pools are found at the bottom of a heavy stream, and we use the shallower ones at the head of the stream as crossing places. When I was new to fishing, it seemed dangerous to cross above the heavy water, but the streams are often shallow, even though they look dangerously swift.

When we found a burn with an abundance of shells, Neil would likely say it was 'cassied' or 'encrusted wi' shells'. The former sounds like an old Scots word, but I'm not sure, having never come across it anywhere else. Donald and his relatives were more likely to say the shells were 'lyin' thick'. If it was a 'dour burn', they could lie ten deep and still not throw a pearl.

At the opposite end of the scale, many burns have been 'wiped oot', or fished to extinction, in which case Neil would say there was 'devil a hait' left. This is another old Scots phrase seldom heard now. If we were sent to such a place having been fed rumours of pearls, it was 'a gooser', from the saying 'a wild goose chase'.

To try to explain the occurrence of pearls in some shells, and the lack of them in others, all the varieties of shape, size and even colour have been minutely categorized. Disappointment has coloured Donald's own names for different types of shells and, apart from changes in fashion over the years, his additions to the stock of older words have become part of the lore of pearling in Rattray and Blairgowrie.

Unmarked, straight shells are generally called 'straights' but are further subdivided to insult them for their lack of pearls. One of the poorest, though not always (the exceptions make nonsense of our theories all the time), are 'beaks' (see drawing on p.114). Beaks

A "Beak"
Fastwater shells

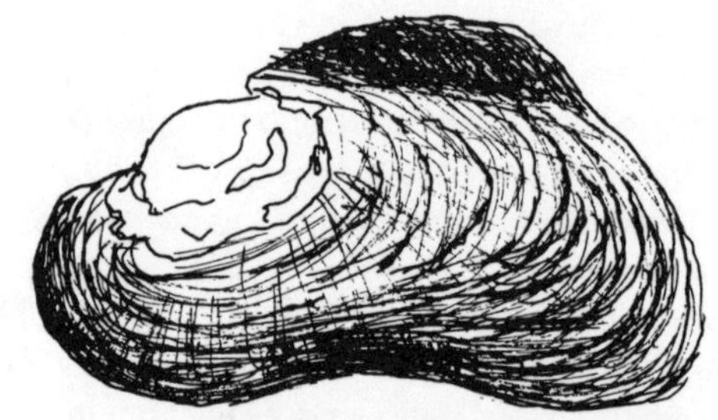

A "Purse"
An aberrant form found in Morar

A "Good Class of Shell"
Found in quieter water

Three varieties of a pearl mussel shell which may sometimes occur in the same river are usually fast-water shells. They may even be the only type of shell found in a fast-flowing river, and occur in the more rapid parts of others. The degree of curvature of the hinge has been described mathematically as the 'arching index'. The greater the arching index, the stronger the current the mussel can withstand. The pearl-fishers discovered this empirically. Comparison of the type of shell found on the bright bottom in fiercer current with those from nearer the bank, by the number of pearls per shell taken, showed the side to be better. Though the two types of bottom may be so well defined that a single pace can carry you from one to the other, it can take a good deal of experience to tell where one ends and the other begins.

The biologists who worked on the arching index dropped shells into varying currents of water and found that the higher the index (the greater the degree of 'beakiness', Donald and Neil would say), the shorter distance they were swept before they touched the bottom: natural selection at work? Donald and Neil took the Lamarckian view that the strength of the current forced them to grow in a curve, and I wonder if that point of view might not be equally valid.

'High hatters', or simply 'hatters', were usually found on a hard bottom where they could not dig in very far, or else in soup where they 'sat high' to avoid being silted over. Sometimes they looked so inviting, big black shells that consistently failed to deliver the goods. You stood for hours lifting them. Donald reckoned that they were laughing at us and called them 'mocking billies'.

'Reds', or otherwise 'mahoganies', were similarly castigated. They were found on bright bottoms and were usually pretty beaky. The name came from the grained reddish-brown colour of the outer skin or periostracum of the shell.

'Good' shells were usually black, had a convex outer margin rather than the concave margin of the beak, were more deeply buried and tended to be found in calmer water in a strip along the bank. The width of this strip of good bottom varies greatly and in some rivers is only a couple of feet wide. Among the 'good class' of shell, more crooks are usual than in the other types.

'Darks' are shells which mimic the characteristics of good shells but hardly ever throw a pearl. There are miles of them in the Spey, and some rivers have nothing else.

Among the normal shells of any river, be they reds, beaks or whatever, are a couple of aberrant types. 'Razorblades' are commonest. They are so narrow in section that the tangs will scarcely grip them. The space available for a pearl to grow is non-existent, and so are the pearls. Another is a kind of hump-backed razorblade/beak, which we call a purse because of its similarity to an old-fashioned leather purse. If anything, they are even less likely to throw than a razorblade. In Morar, Neil and Donald found a river full of purses. It was only a few feet wide, yet in places it was twenty feet deep and so clear that the mass of little purses could be seen quite clearly, crouching on what Donald called a 'sulphuric bottom'. They didn't get a seed.

The ultimate mockery was to be sent on a gooser to a burn that was cassied with fat, black shells that had something odd about them which was apparent before you even set foot in the water. Instead of being aligned, for the most part, with the current, they lay idly on their sides, or on their backs, facing any way the fancy took them. They were very easily opened and had orange meat inside instead of the pale fawn and brown of the pearl mussel's body. Andra called them 'scregalhechans', or 'hechans' for short. They were duck mussels and seldom threw pearls. We went to a river by Ripley Castle in Yorkshire some years ago, and Donald recognized the hechans instantly by their posture, without even getting down from the railway bridge on which we stood.

Apart from opening a shell and finding a big pearl, a pearl-fisher's most exciting moment is when he lifts a good crook. It can lead to bitter disappointment when it doesn't throw the expected pearl. Practised fishers can pick out the crooks on the bottom among perhaps hundreds of straights. The beginner tends to classify any shell with a mark on it as a crook, but many marks are caused by shifting stones or the feet of cattle. We call these 'tramped crooks', and they come under the general heading of fake crooks.

To have any chance of a pearl, a shell should normally have what we call a 'draw', or 'run', that originates in the direction of the oldest, most eroded umbonal region of the hinge. The draw radiates from here towards the outer margin. (See the illustration on p.118.)

Andra's thin black moustache inspired Donald's name for a type of crook in which the run is in the form of a narrow groove or fold. 'Zits' crook is now the accepted term among all of us.

Unfortunately, although the mussel contorts its shell quite spectacularly as though an enormous pearl was a foregone conclusion, it is more often the opposite case. If there is a pearl in a zits, it is usually near the margin of the shell, and as a result is a dull brown colour.

Bad buckling of the shell produces 'fierce crooks', as we call these whose deformity renders them almost unrecognizable as mussels. Donald's maxim is that the fiercer the crooks, the fewer the pearls. It certainly seems to be true, although fierce crooks are still exciting when you first see them. On more than one occasion I have sat down for an opening with over thirty crooks – and I mean real crooks: backriggs, heavy siders, McNab's Fingers, zits, humph'n'flats, or whatever you care to call them – in one bagful. As I sit opening them (or at least just prising them slightly), if I come on a crook, I lay it aside. Any shells with slight buckles or possible marks go in a second heap to be opened after the straights. It is this pile which gives the greatest proportion of pearls, and the fiercest crooks may produce fewer than even the straights on a lucky day when 'straights are throwing'.

Straights find their way into the bag because many crooks are not obvious. The shell may attract attention for some indefinable reason and is lifted. If it is not marked in some way, it could get put in the bag anyway. On an exceptional day I've seen a man get most of his pearls in the straights, but for those who kill the shells to look for their pearls, killing the straights is killing the river. As with all man's depredations on nature, rather than suffer one bad day now and then, the pearl-fisher takes as much as he can to avoid it, and stores up a lifetime of bad days for the future.

I'd better explain the other crooks before going on too far. The classic is 'heavy sider', especially if it has 'fell in'. I believe that this is what some fishers call a 'humph'n'flat' because it has a hump on one side and is flat on the other. Most of these deformities occur in the part of the shell which protrudes from the river bed. Neil once showed me a good crook in which the pearl, he said, was on the 'wrong side'. At that time I didn't appreciate this rarity, which had nothing to do with right or left. The pearls usually sit on the 'fell-in' side of the shell, but this one was on the 'heavy' side. A careless glance could have passed over it, and the shell would have been thrown back.

Three views of a "Fell-in" crook

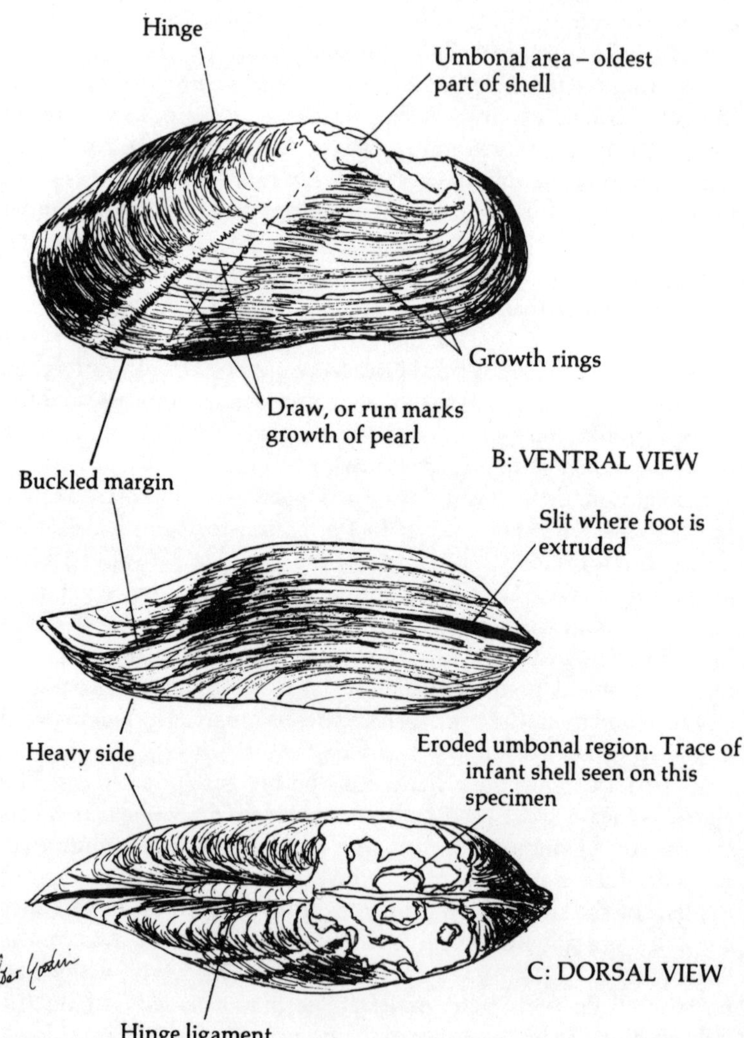

When a Rattray man, Jimmy McNab, had a finger amputated, Donald must have instantly spotted its resemblance to a grossly deformed crook in which the sharper, upward-facing end grows back in on itself. Everyone calls it a McNab's finger now. They very seldom throw a decent pearl, though I once had a pair of five-grain balls in one.

'Bananas' didn't really merit being called crooks. They were crooked all right but didn't have a run or draw on them, so seldom threw pearls. One evening, we had just finished fishing 'The Smelly Field' at the Spey and were having an opening. My only crook was instantly pounced on by Donald, who denounced it as a 'useless banana'. I opened it last and got a six-grain ball to get my revenge. It is such a rare occurrence to get a pearl in one that they no longer cause any excitement, but they go in the bag just in case. On a bad day, even fake crooks are something to look forward to.

Finally to the pearls themselves. What we call a bottle of pearls is something of an exaggeration. The bottle is usually only a small pill bottle or an old-fashioned glass aspirin bottle, and the pearls would be two or three dozen nice pearls rolling around the bottom. None of us likes using brown pill bottles because they don't show the pearls off.

When the pearls are taken out of the shell, great care has to be taken. The pearl's sac is quite elastic and slides about in the mantle which becomes detached from the shell. Small pearls stick to the fingers and the cap of the bottle, and all of them are attracted towards dark corners, thick piled carpets, long grass and piles of dead leaves. They are carefully popped out into the glass of the upturned jug, then transferred to the bottle, where they are kept in a little water. The water keeps the pearls 'fresh'. If pearls are allowed to dry straight from the shell without being rubbed gently with a soft cloth, they can become coated with a dull watermark, though it is easily removed by wetting them again.

Keeping the pearls in water has a more useful function. Many pearls are not pure – that is, they have a fawn or brown ring or spot on them. It can be caused by their being situated near to the edge of the shell, where there is a ring of brown mother of pearl that has no lustre. Sometimes, though there is a considerable area of clear, lustrous white, as the water content of the pearl falls, the dull ring creeps over the clear part, often leaving only a tiny spot.

It is preferable for this to happen after you've been paid for it.

The majority of jewellers calculate the value of pearls by assigning prices per grain weight to each of several basic shapes. A grain is a quarter of a carat, and there are 5,760 grains to the jeweller's pound, which, incidentally, has only twelve ounces in it.

A few jewellers used a card punched with holes corresponding to the grain weight of round pearls. As the commonest freshwater pearls are flattened on one side, this method was very favourable to the fisher. We judged the weight of our haul by guessing them individually, and the two Marys were seldom far out in estimating the total in the bottle before they took them to the jeweller. It is not easy to estimate the weight of such variable shapes. Even the round pearls are difficult. For example, a five-grain ball is approximately six millimetres in diameter, and a ten-grain one is about 7½ millimetres across.

The basic shapes, starting with the commonest, are buttons, barrels, vunks, balls and drops. Buttons, called 'boutons' by the jewellers, are round, flat-bottomed pearls with conical tops of varying height. Elongated, approximately cylindrical pearls we call barrels. They are just about as common as buttons but tend to be less useful to the jeweller. It is characteristic of barrels for their central portion to be marked with a brown ring or a groove-like constriction. Another common type is an 'ender', which possesses a small lustrous 'heid' on a brown shank. If it is not a creeper, the head can be sawn off to make a button pearl. Barrels with a fairly broad brown ring round them are sometimes sawn into two buttons by cutting through the ring.

I once had a ten-grain barrel with a dark ring round it. At the best it was worth, at that time, £1 a grain. We were getting £2 a grain for buttons, so I gently squeezed it in between soft wood blocks in the vice and hacksawed it in two. The ends filed off and polished with jewellers' rouge, leaving two four-grain buttons that were well worth the hour's work.

Some barrels have several constrictions and ridges around them and look as if they have been turned on a lathe.

'Vunk' is our version of what jewellers call 'baroque' pearls. They are lustrous pearls but are shapeless, asymmetrical and seemingly useless. The Perth jewellers to whom Donald and Neil sold most of the pearls enjoyed the challenge of finding a design to accommodate these unusual shapes, such as the abdomen of a gold beetle with enamel wings.

Anything remotely egg-shaped we call a drop. They are about as scarce as round pearls, or 'balls'. Balls are generally the most valuable grade and form around five per cent of the total find. I think they are formed by the growing pearl having freedom to revolve in its sac in any direction. Mother-of-pearl is laid down evenly on its surface. Buttons are found with their flat bottom towards the side of the shell on which they sit. They probably turn on their bottom, while barrels roll in the sac on their side.

Evidence for this theory came from observing pearls that grew on the edge of the shell. I once got a fifteen-grain button in the Spey that had just become stuck to the edge of the shell. It had not yet become a real 'sticker' and was easily detached. Most of the pearl was clear and lustrous, but where its rim overlapped the brown strip round the edge of the shell, it had a matching brown mark. This indicated that the pearl had remained untarnished while free in its sac. Other buttons often have brown bottoms which creep up the side to a varying degree. If only a tiny spot of white is left, they're called a 'teddy bear's e'e'. The bottom of the pearl, nearest the shell, is the broadest and most likely to pick up brown discolouration. If the button pearl were stationary, like the big one I mentioned previously, the brown could not possibly travel all round its base. Pearls that do become stationary for some reason are gradually buried into the shell.

About three quarters of the total pearls taken are brown or reddish in colour and have no lustre. We can spot a potential brown pearl by the exterior of the shell. A zits crook, or any shell with a thin draw that extends right to the edge, is the sign we look for. As pearls are coated with the same material as the part of the shell they sit in, white pearls are found deeper in than brown and fawn ones. Of course, upsets still occur. Donald's despairing cry: 'Pure broon an' a mile doon!' rings in my ears as I write. So much shell-building material may be diverted to the pearl that the shell beneath it is thin, and the darker under layers, or even the horn that lies between the mother-of-pearl and the black outer skin, may be exposed. We say the pearl is 'bored in'. For some reason, the mantle seems sensitive to this state and, even well away from the margin can produce brown mother-of-pearl in sufficient quantities to ruin pearl's value.

Fawn pearls are a terrible disappointment. When the shell is prised just sufficiently to see the pearl but not kill the mussel, it is hard to tell a fawn pearl from a white one through the thin sac. Do you pop out a pearl that turns out to be worthless, yet could be valuable in three years time, or risk throwing something worth £100 back in the river? It has long been my opinion that fawn pearls are browns that are turning white, though most of my fellow fishers scoff at this idea. However, any attempt to clean a fawn by dissolving the top layers with spirts of salt, or scraping them away, always reveals darker layers beneath. The hypothesis could be proven one way or the other by taking some, big white pearls and sawing them in half to see if any are brown inside!

What I think happens is that brown pearls which grow to any size on the margin without becoming stickers – that is, they remain in the sac – are too large to occupy the narrow angle formed by the meeting of the valves. They are steadily forced back into the region where white mother-of-pearl is laid down and are coated with white nacre, as the pearl material is called.

Killing shells is a bad policy anyway, but killing shells with brown or fawn pearls in them, or even taking these pearls out, is particularly stupid. Taking them to a safe place to allow the process to continue to until they are clear makes more sense. Seed pearls could be dealt with in the same way. I have bottles of brown pearls, fawns, creepers, enders and teddy bear's e'es, which could have been worth tens of thousands of pounds if I'd practised in the early days what I preach now.

As I've already said, the majority of pearls are found in the part of the shell that protrudes from the river bed – actually its posterior. The buried portion we call the 'heel', which is appropriate in a way because it is where the animal's foot is extruded. Pearls do occur in the heel occasionally, though they generally take the form of a mass of milky 'dirt', or a single 'tooth'. Though white, they have little or no lustre. Now and then, a good pearl is found near the foot. It is hard to see when you prise the mussel about half an inch to avoid killing it. This rare occurrence is used as an argument for opening all shells wide and killing them. Fishers who do this feel round the inside of both valves with their thumbs, as well as making a quick visual inspection for bulges in the mantle. They are less likely to miss a pearl now and then, but I see no point in mass extermination as a means of avoiding such a paltry loss.

Only two more specific types of brown pearl occur to me. A brown baroque pearl with lumps all over it, or the appearance of a brain, was not even thrown in the bottom of the bag with the other browns. 'Asteroids' were utterly useless, unless you were one of those who rejected indigestion tablets in favour of ground pearls.

Apart from the general sneering remark 'dog's brown', when a crook had let them down, Donald and Neil would use an even more insulting comparison if the expected ten-grain ball turned out to be a long reddish-brown barrel. 'Red dog's carrie, ged!' likened the pearl to the male organ of a dog.

A question we are frequently asked is, do we ever find any black pearls and are they very valuable? Though I'm forced to say that most people's notions concerning them belong to the realm of myth and fantasy, the answer is, surprisingly, yes to the first and no to the second question.

I mentioned earlier that the mantle, the skin lining the inside of the shell, continuously lays down new mother-of-pearl, or nacre, in the shell, and it adds rings of new growth to the edge. The shell actually has three distinct layers: nacre inside, then a layer resembling horn, or nail (it has the same smell when burnt), then the outer periostracum, which is chitin. Chitin is the substance from which the exoskeleton of insects is constructed. It is extremely time-resistant and remains long after the acid waters of the pearl mussels' habitat have dissolved away the rest the shell. It can remain long enough to become buried and provides fossil imprints of mussels in ancient sedimentary rocks. Since the outside layer had to be made by the edge of the mantle, it occasionally happens that some of the chitin finds its way into a pearl sac where it may darken a brown pearl or even form a small black pearl of pure chitin. These are flaky, lustreless and totally without value. There is no freshwater equivalent of the rare inky blue South Seas "black" pearls.

Cultured pearls are without doubt beautiful. They are predictably beautiful, and their perfection is of little consequence through being taken for granted. Compared with this uniformity, the wide range of colour, shape, size and lustre of the pearls of the northern rivers is bewildering. Perfection is more highly prized for its rarity, and the only greater rarity among freshwater pearls is a perfect match. There is nothing manufactured about them, and this is reflected in their prices, which I already knew were far above those of cultured pearls. As far as Donald was concerned, man's interference by putting a nucleus in an oyster, around which the pearl still grew naturally, was nothing short of manufacturing 'artificial' pearls.

One day's fishing in one river could produce an amazing variety of colours in the bottle. They could be white, silver, grey, pink, steely blue, purple like pale heather bells and very occasionally pale orange. We called these 'sun pearls'. Donald's Mary (as opposed to Mary McGregor, Neil's wife under her maiden name) was very fond of them. Whenever there was one in the bottle, it was put into the jeweller's with the rest and she bought it from the pool for the jeweller's valuation.

One of the rarest shades among the river pearls is the creamy colour of the cultured oyster pearls. It is uncommon enough to be a fairly safe way of differentiating them without resorting to cutting them or exposing the coarser growth rings of the oyster pearls by means of X-rays.

Like other fishermen, especially the trawlermen, pearl-fishers are a superstitious lot. In particular, to avoid marring a day's fishing, certain animals were to be either avoided or, in some cases, not even referred to. I had to learn these taboos very early on, out of respect for my colleagues, if not for my own belief, and possibly just in case they were right! I bring appalling weather, terrible misfortune and untold hardship on myself by listing them here.

Category one contains the unmentionables. Crocodiles don't do too much harm as they are unlikely to find their way into the conversation on the way to the river, but it has been known. Eels and snakes can be glossed over by the term 'coilers'. Mentioning adders is a likely source of trouble, and there is a sign on the way to the Spey which tells tourists stopping in layby to beware of them. Someone usually managed to comment on it or to trick us all into looking that way. Donkeys were more dangerous when seen than when spoken about, though they still referred to as 'MacGillicuddys', just in case. Goats used to be less of a problem but are more common nowadays. Their connection with 'The Hornéd One' was bound to be a bad influence. As with donkeys, if you saw one, you weren't to look, though how this was to be achieved, I've never discovered. The pike was about the worst thing in the animal line that could ever be mentioned. Even a veiled reference to 'himself' was no way of disguising it. Everyone knew that was the end of your chance of a good day, and morale sank.

Bagpipes are not unlucky in themselves. They could lie about the house for years and do no harm. Even unscrewing the chanter and practising for an hour or two probably wouldn't matter. According to Donald, it is the drones that do the damage. He maintains that they draw dark clouds, it rains, the rivers rise and we can't fish. Of course, his uncle Alec, of whom I've already spoken, was a piper and lived only two doors from Donald and Neil. Between his practising and the distant sound of the Blairgowrie pipe band drifting up from the Well Meadow on Saturdays in the summer, there was little chance of clear skies.

One of the worst things to befall a pearl fisher, or a traveller, was to meet a MacPhee, or even to hear his name spoken. We always seemed to run into a certain Donald MacPhee. It was as though he spent his day parading round the town *trying* to be seen by as many people as possible. Even on the way to Perth we would come on him hitching a lift that way, and couldn't avoid picking him up. The belief runs so deep that the clan of MacPhee, MacPhie, McAfee, or whatever, are nicknamed after the curse that 'Blind Pugh' brought to 'Billy Bones' in the opening of *Treasure Island*: 'The Black Spot'. MacPhees who are travellers are so acutely aware of the potency of their name that, out of deference to their fellow travellers' feelings, they refuse to say it when asked who they are. To bear the name is bad enough; to be forced to speak it is to be doubly cursed. This, of course, identified them immediately.

Donald calls Donald MacPhee 'Donald Macker' or 'Donald Mackinfaces' to avoid disaster. Neil once asked the name of a pearler he met in Glen Lyon. The man shuffled in embarrassment till Neil said at last: 'Never mind. I think I ken it anyway.' The poor man muttered gruffly: 'I ken, I ken.'

On the way to the shells it was considered bad luck to have to go back for something. Even if it meant someone had to go hungry or fish without waders, it was seen as an omen that we should not have set out in the first place. The only grudging exception to this was a forgotten jug. A stick could be cut at the roadside; one day without waders could be borne, even in cold weather; a jersey could be turned into a bag; but to be unable see the bottom of the river, you might as well not be there at all.

12. Mull and the Black Mount

In the tradition of the pearl-fishers, another man who used to fish with Donald and Neil sometimes found shells on Mull while honeymooning on the island. However, to his discredit, he didn't actually fish the river. We tried it during a dry spell in May, though the wet west coast was always a risk.

Gordon Wilson, Davy Bell and Ronald 'Tawser' MacDonald were on holiday and came too. Tawser had been working among dried potato powder in the cannery, and Donald temporarily nicknamed him 'The Wondermasher' during the trip. Six people and their gear was more than usual for one car, but we couldn't take two on the ferry. Neil was more concerned about 'coilers' (for which Mull is renowned in his opinion) than logistical problems with the car.

'I'll no sit doon till we get back tae the mainland,' he stated emphatically. 'I'll open my shells standin' in the burn, or sittin'on an island.'

'It's surely not that bad for ...' Neil's warning glance stopped me from mentioning the unmentionable. 'You'd think we were going to be knee deep in them the minute we stepped off the ferry,' I laughed. 'Anyway, islands are no use. They can swim, you know.'

'I'll no be takin' any chances. They're nesty wee beasts, ye ken, an' ye're a lang way fae a hospital.'

We rose about five and left before six to get a 9 a.m. ferry from Oban, over a hundred miles away. It was a beautifully clear morning, fresh, calm and with promising clear skies as far ahead as we could see. Above Loch Tay we could see Cruachan, many miles ahead and still standing sharp against the blue western skies.

The road was empty, and when we reached the Dochart above Killin, the new road let us make up time lost in the windings of

Strathtay and the Loch Tay road. Beyond Tyndrum, turning left, we entered the Loch Awe catchment. By the huge loch, the road straddled small inlets on spindly bridges, and skirted low cliffs on rocky ledges blasted to help straighten its path along the ragged shore. The River Awe was supposed to have pearl mussels in it, but it squeezed through the narrow, scree-strewn Pass of Brander too steeply for them to survive there, and there was little level ground before it reached the sea.

We got to Oban twenty minutes before the ferry left. The bar opened as soon as the ship was under way, and we went below for a drink. I went back on deck to watch the little fishing port receding behind us, wearing the grey stone circle of McCaig's Folly like a crown. The lofty domes of Mull's hills seemed to keep their distance as we slid nearer on the glassy sea.

Landing at Craignure on the east coast, we travelled north on a single-track road. Across the Sound of Mull, where the hills of Morven were slashed by the mouth of Loch Aline, another ferry was coming from there, heading straight for us.

'Ged, the folk never telt us aboot that ferry,' Neil complained. 'I bet it's cheaper than the ane fae Oban.'

Not far from the ferry a track led up a long, straight glen leading far into the round, bare hills of the interior. We followed it a little way, but the river was a mass of gravel. Further up the main road was a turning that took us up a small, wooded glen with a promising little burn, but it rapidly gave way to a tumbling stream that was no use to us. The unclassified road was better than the A848 that we'd been on, so we carried on over an empty moorland plateau that gradually began to slope down to the north.

Gordon volunteered to have a look at a burn we glimpsed in the shallow glen, and we took the car downstream. We walked about a mile across rank heather and tussocks of coarse grass before suddenly coming on the river, winding gently across the flat moor. It was surprisingly deep in parts and had a few big shells lying in the deepest corners, sitting in bare, gravelly sand. Some pools were too deep to wade, and we had to try to reach the shells off the side of steep banks of loose shingle.

I wanted to take a photograph of everyone at the riverside, but there was still no sign of Gordon. We fished on beyond the car but still didn't see him, so I took the picture without him. Tired and hungry, we headed back to the car, with Neil watching every step of the way for adders. He had kept his promise never to sit down, and opened his shells on rocks and islets. It was dull and cool by this time, and we were so weary when we got to the road that even Neil lay down, after examining the short turf with exaggerated care. We waited over half an hour in the sour breeze till Gordon appeared in the distance. We'd been getting a little concerned and were thinking of rousing ourselves to go and look for him.

'Tons o' shells up there, ged. D'you boys get anything?' he asked with cheerful lack of concern.

'They'd be useless reds up there,' Donald snorted. 'Ye wouldnae get a seed in them.'

'What did you get?' Gordon asked. We'd got nothing at all.

'Aye well, shells were scarce doon there,' Donald muttered by way of excuse.

Tired though we were, we looked at the bottom end of the river where it entered a shallow sea loch. It was full of green algae and black rocks, but there were no shells. Continuing round the north-western corner of the island, past the Isle of Ulva, we headed for the mountainous southern part of Mull. The River Coladoir looked all right on paper but flowed through a deep glen beyond Ben More.

We circled the shores of Loch na Keal. On the south shore, huge outriders of the hills crept nearer the sea till they squeezed out the narrow cultivated strip. Just beyond the hamlet of Derryguaig, where the hills plunged straight to the sea, a huge boulder sat on the last bit of flat ground. It had a low stone wall round it. I was pondering this enigma when Donald let out a yell.

'It's a wee hoose, ged! That stane's rolled recht on it.'

Much later I read the story. The people of Derryguaig had built the croft house for a young married couple to move into after their wedding. In the early hours of their wedding night, the boulder rolled onto the house, covering all but the front and side walls. The croft became their grave, and the boulder its marker.

Grassy scree slopes hung dangerously over the road beyond the headland, and on the crags above, larger chunks waited to plummet to the sea. On the western sea, beyond the nearest islands, lay Ulva, Little Colonsay and Staffa, and just off the Ross of Mull was Iona. Between us and the Ross of Mull the sea had devoured part of a sixteen-hundred-foot hill to leave a thousand-foot cliff. The road cut inland through a narrow glen and came out on the wild shore of Loch Scridain. At the head of this loch the Coladoir River entered the sea. Cloud clung darkly to Ben More, casting huge purple shadows into Glen More, distorting distance and perspective.

On reaching the 'other' main road we crossed the river twice and saw that it was no good.

'A rattle o' boulders, ged,' Donald muttered. 'A bed o' railway metal.'

It was a desolate bed of harsh, angular gravel, scoured from the side of the glen. The ferry sailed about nine, and we were only fifteen miles from it with about three hours to wait. We decided to go back up the east coast to look at a couple of burns near Tobermory. There were no shells in the first burn, and it was nearly time to leave. Rather than spend the night on the island to look at one doubtful burn, we turned back, without a seed to take home from Mull.

Dusk was falling as the ferry slid smoothly out between Lismore Island and Mull, into the Firth of Lorn. Even here, exposed to the Atlantic, the swell was as lethargic as syrup. We went below for a drink, and it was dark when we came into Oban. We wandered the streets for a while, trying in vain to find a place where we could get a late drink.

'Dodie and Lizzie are whelking up this way. If we find them, at least we'll get a cup o' tea and somewhere tae lie doon.' Donald's cousin was married to a man who made a living collecting shellfish on the west coast.

We drove north over Loch Etive, through the district of Benderloch, round Loch Creran. There was no sign of Dodie and Lizzie's caravan among the other travellers in the laybys along the coast, so we camped on a broad verge on the shore of Loch Leven.

In the morning Neil and I went down to the beach to gather whelks (winkles in England). A thin mist hung, incandescent with the rising sun. The hills of Glencoe could be vaguely discerned through the glare. It didn't take us long to reach the foot of the glen. In the early morning light, with the snow tops clearly defined against the blue sky and hanging over the village, the scene had an unreal, Swiss postcard look to it. Glencoe did not cast the same spell in brilliant sunshine as we passed beneath the ruined MacDonald clachan. The scene of the massacre needed a grey drizzle.

Climbing between the crowded hills, we came out on a huge moorland plateau. This was Rannoch Moor. On the right were the hills surrounding the head of Glen Etive. They soared abruptly from the moor, itself nearly a thousand feet about sea-level. Six or seven miles ahead, over heather, bracken, grass and bog, rose the Grampians at the source of the Lyon.

We were going to fish the Black Mount, where Donald's father and uncle had fished before him. They used to take a train from Perth to Dunblane, then up Strathyre and Glen Dochart to Rannoch Station, if they wanted to fish the Gaur. This left them a twelve-mile walk along Loch Laidon and past Loch Bà, to the Black Mount. Otherwise they would leave the train at Bridge of Orchy. From here they could fish the now extinct Orchy or walk ten miles to the Black Mount over the old road which crosses the river further upstream. The latter seems the most likely as shells are more common (at least they were) near the new road. The nearer you get to the path of the old one, the scarcer the shells become, even though the bottom is better. Here, only twelve miles from the west coast at the head of Loch Etive, the water finds its way to the east coast through the Tummel and Tay. The shells, however, are small, red 'beaks' in the main part, typical of the western rivers. One part of the river is separated from the Orchy drainage by only fifty feet in height and a few hundred yards distance, so it may have been captured by the eastern-flowing system in early post-glacial times.

We left the car in a hollow scooped in the bank at the side of the road, close to a bridge. Tawser had spent a sleepless night smoking in the car and wasn't feeling at all well.

'I'm chokit,' he complained, lighting another cigarette as we tucked into cold beans and dry bread.

'The Wondermasher's feach'd[1] ged,' Donald tittered from the other side of the car.' He was pechin'[2] and pantin' a' necht, but he

[1] Finished.
[2] Puffing.

couldnae stop sookin' at reek.[1] Twenty fags tae get through the necht, ged.'

'I'll gie you Wondermasher,' Tawser spluttered, red-faced. He called after us as we left. 'You boys fish up the way, and leave me a bit near the car.'

Donald, Neil, Davy, Gordon and I set off past the first part of the river and skirted the first of a series of lochans it flowed through. The ground was broken and difficult. Between rocky hummocks were bogs or areas of dry peat cracked into deep crevices with black ooze in the bottom. The bleached roots and stumps of the Scots pines of the almost vanished Caledonian Forest protruded from the sides of the banks. On level ground, huge tussocks of coarse grass made walking a weary succession of stumbles and curses. The sun blazed down from the cloudless sky, making it a pleasure to get into the cold water. Socks and trousers were saturated with sweat inside our waders.

We began fishing, each taking a side of a deep stretch, or stringing out where it was narrow and we started getting in each other's way.

'Awfy reds in this burn,' Donald commented. 'They're slippy wee beaks, but ye can aye get a crook.'

He might have got crooks but I wasn't finding it easy. The river bottom was a reddish, gravelly sand lying between slippy rocks and packed with shells. Stringy algal growth flickered and danced from rock and shell alike, and though they were easily seen, the eyes soon wearied of searching for a crook among thousands of 'straights'. In calm pools, or behind rocks as big as a bus, the shells appeared as slits in a silt of peat and windblown dead grass. You couldn't see them till they were at the surface, and if you didn't get them first time, the silt rose in a cloud, and they retreated deeper into it. The tangs had to be well set: too close and they forced the shell deep into the soft bottom, too loose and it was impossible to extract them from between stones and rocks.

The shells became very scarce. The water was slow, and the bottom, free of rocks and stones, was a pure, yellow sand laid in ripples like a beach with the tide going out. On one side was a long bank of weed, its long, olive-green blades leaning downstream in

[1]Smoke.

the gentle current, swaying like a Siamese dancer. The sandy calm led into a lochan with a similar bottom. Skirting its shore, we soon came to where the river entered, and I sat down for an opening and to ease my back before fishing on. Despite my earlier difficulties, some nice buttons lay on top of the jug, ready for the bottle. Content, I sat for a while watching the others fishing on ahead towards the great cradle of Choireach a' Bà, the birthplace of the river.

Wind and rain, rightful elements of the high moor, were suspended above the sea, far to the west of the long striding ridge of Aonach Mòr. From here they would fall on the land to reclaim it from the vicarious sunlit calm that possessed it now. Away from the chatter of water on stone, the babble of our voices desecrated a stillness that even the birds hardly broke that day.

In six hours away from the car we'd covered nearly five miles of river but were only two miles from our starting point in a straight line. Though we'd not eaten, we'd drunk freely of the pure water of the river, dipping our jugs in like huge tankards. There was no human habitation on the first fourteen miles of the river, nor any of its tributaries, so the most fastidious drank freely.

The car was long out of sight when we turned back towards the road. Walking briskly over the rough ground on a hot day, in waders, soon had us in a lather of sweat. Donald took off his waders and socks, stuck his feet into his sawn-off wellington overboots and strode on in obvious relief.

'Ged! He's no feared o' coilers,' commented an amazed Neil. 'I'd suffer any amount o' heat and I wouldnae tak' my boots off for Britain.' His over-healthy respect for adders was the main reason for our speed.

When we came to peat bogs at the head of the long fingers of water branching from the lochans, Donald began to experience difficulties. The stinking black ooze filled his wading boots and covered the bottom of his trousers, and taking the long way round was his only means of avoiding it. It took an hour of non-stop fast walking to reach the car. Tawser was lying in it half asleep.

'I fished a wee while, but I was still chokit,' he told us. 'Those boys on the loch came over for a crack,' he said, pointing to a dinghy on Loch Bà, then, turning to Donald, 'They're tinks and they ken you. Ane o' them said: "I ken Donald McGregor; a bonny pearl-fisher, ged;" ' Tawser was still smarting from Donald's 'Wondermasher' taunts.

Though we'd got nothing on Mull, and Tawser had been too unwell to contribute much to the day at the Black Mount, we'd done quite well overall. For once, I'd made a reasonable contribution to the bottle. The pearls were small but were very bright and would fetch a good price.

We stowed the gear and turned for home. The road descended from the high moor in a series of looping bends to the shore of Loch Tulla, following its outflow, the River Orchy, a little way. It looked too fast and rocky to be a good burn but had been at one time apparently. Turning east out of Glen Orchy, we drove up a scree-strewn glen, gazing across the U-shaped valley at the railway line's contortions as it hugged the contours on the slow climb to Glen Fillan.

The bare, domed hills above the railway fascinated Donald. He took a boyish delight in the idea of setting a big tractor tyre rolling down them, imagining it buckling and bounding over rock and gully, leaping the track and the river to come to rest on the road.

13. Bad Day in Kintyre

After a spell of good weather in late May, it was less risky to try rivers beyond our 'local area' of about sixty miles radius. Tawser's mother had given him the names of rivers his grandfather had fished, and he was very keen to see them for himself. His grandfather had fished all over Scotland, judging from the names of rivers we saw on a list Tawser's mother wrote out. The family had boasted that they'd never eaten three-day-old soup. Once, however, they were told of a great pearl burn deep in the hills, miles from the nearest road. For three days they wandered through a series of uninhabited glens, looking in vain for this river. On the third day, the only food left was in the round iron soup-pot. They swallowed it along with their pride.

This particular river, the Carradale, was in the extreme south-west of Argyll, not far from Campbeltown. There was very little chance of melted snow affecting rivers there, and though rain was always a risk in the west, there was more likelihood of the hills of nearby Arran catching it than the lower land on Kintyre.

With Davy Bell, his brother Pete and Tawser, plus the usual rations and camping stuff, we decided to take two cars. There were other rivers we could fish *en route*, and six of us could never hope to get into one car with everything needed for several nights away and a long drive. Neil and Donald were familiar with the road as far as Lochgilphead. We drove along the sombre, forested shores of Loch Earn to Lochearnhead, then north to Glen Dochart just above the falls at Killin. Donald pointed out a solitary chimneybreast above the road in Glen Dochart which he told me was the remains of one of Rob Roy's homes, known to few McGregors and even fewer outsiders.

We forked left down Glen Falloch, passing through Crianlarich without my noticing. I'd expected more of a place signposted sixty miles back in Perth, while Blairgowrie, only fifteen miles from Perth and with five times the population of Crianlarich, was not mentioned.

We followed the winding road down the shores of Loch Lomond. Each headland offered glimpses of the misted waters. Less than half way down the loch we had to leave its shores to cut off the Cowall Peninsula, where the thirty-mile prongs of Loch Fyne and Loch Long stab deep into the Argyll coast. It was cold, but the sun shone from clear skies on Loch Fyne and the Sound of Bute. The hills of Arran and Bute rose purple from a blue sea, clear in the clean, calm air. The port of Tarbert looked as though it had been scrubbed from top to bottom, and the water in the harbour lay like blue stained glass.

Below the isthmus connecting Knapdale and Kintyre, we were directly opposite the Isle of Arran. Its purple and brown hills, with their inky shadows, basked in the luminous serenity of a calm, sunlit sea. For ten miles we drove with this vision floating in a sea of light on our left, then we cut inland to a river valley. Following it south, almost to the sea again, we came to a bridge by a tiny church among trees. This was the hamlet of Saddel on the Carradale Water.

Waders on, I started into a deep corner while Donald pranced along the bank behind in a purely supervisory capacity. There was no sign of shells, and none of the others fishing below the bridge had any luck either. A mile upstream, where the river ran through a forest, it was no better.

Neil, Davy and I wanted to keep going south to Campbeltown, but the other three wanted to go home. We acquiesced, and Neil drove after Donald in grim silence.

At dusk we stopped at a little harbour pub in Tarbert, from which the sound of accordion and loud drumming erupted as we made for the door. One end of the long bar was crammed with fishermen, leaving a space for the entertainers at the other. Mistaking us for crew of a 'foreign' boat, one of the locals held up his whisky glass and winked: 'You lads waiting for the tide?' At this point the music started, and further conversation was impossible. We realized why there was so much room at the end of the bar. The drummer was surrounded by whisky glasses, mostly empty, and was trying to work his way systematically through the

Above; Wearing full pearl-fishing regalia, from left to right: Neil McCormick, Davy Bell, Ronald MacDonald, and Donald McGregor at the River Bellart, Mull. *Below*; Neil McCormick scanning the bottom for crooks, below Cromdale Bridge, River Spey, Morayshire.

The River Moidart in Glen Moidart, south-west Inverness-shire. Home of the beaks.

The Falls of Dochart, Killin, Perthshire.

The Auld Road home. Looking south towards Lochnagar down the old military road, now the A939.

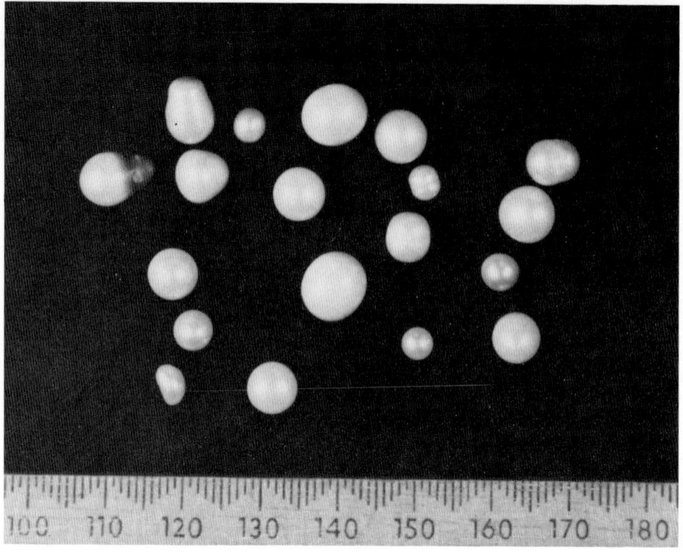

River pearls against a mm. rule. The largest is an eighteen-grain drop from the Spey.

FRESHWATER PEARLS MOUNTED INTO FINE JEWELLERY BY A. & G. CAIRNCROSS, PERTH.
(*left*) Gold and pearl brooch representing rowan leaves and berries.
(*right*) A unique black opal and pearl pendant. Actual size.

full ones. The more he downed, the louder he became. He went on after the accordion had stopped and was bursting into sudden rolls that made everyone jump, even when his partner had gone to the toilet.

None of the places we chanced on seemed never to have heard of licensing laws, and this was no exception. An hour after closing time it was still going strong. The tide was obviously not right yet.

When we went out, Pete Bell and Tawser kept by Donald. They made for Donald and Neil's car, and Neil suddenly exploded: 'Why the fuck did ye stand a' necht in the pub when ye kent fine ye were gaein' hame?' he barked.

'The burns are nae use in this void. I'm mackin' for hame. You boys can dae what ye like,' muttered Donald.

He jumped into the car, in which Pete and Tawser were already ensconced, and started it. I saw Neil's silence had been symptomatic of an undercurrent of seething rage. With a roar: 'Stone mad idiot!' he dived at the car as it moved off, and tore the rubber ski-rack of tangs from the roof. We clipped it to my car and drove on to find a campsite.

'God curse them!' Neil muttered. 'They've got a' the meat, ged! I took the tangs tae stop them fishing, and forgot the meat was in the boot. There's nae shop for miles, ged.' He lapsed into silence.

'Why did Pete and Tawser go with him?' I asked.

'They've tae be at work in the morning,' Davy explained.

'I dinnae ken why they come when they ken fine we're awa' for the necht, or longer.' Neil was cooling off. 'Donald tak's moich turns like that noo an' again.'

We drove on till, at the head of Loch Long, tiredness began to overtake us. Fifty miles from Tarbert, just before Arrochar, we swung over a little burn at the end of the loch, and our headlights caught a couple of tents beyond the bridge. We pulled off the road, parked by a little track up the burn side and put up the tent near the others. It was about one in the morning and, though starving and cold, we fell asleep immediately.

In the morning it was dull and raw, with a slight drizzle. It was hard to keep warm without food, so we walked over the road to the sea and filled our jugs with whelks and mussels. We boiled these on a fire and the primus. While they were cooking, our nearest neighbours, two Glaswegian lads, took pity on us and shared their sausages and bacon with us. Warmed by the hospitality, we sat and talked a while before driving north, leaving a trail of whelk shells behind us.

'How aboot fishing the Lyon on the way hame?' Neil suggested.

Davy and I agreed, and we retraced our route to Glen Dochart, following the river right down into Killin, where we bought pies and bridies. The whelks had run out, and the breakfast had worn off. We held on down Loch Tay till we reached a tiny road that cuts over a shoulder of Ben Lawers to come out at Bridge of Balgie in Glen Lyon. On the long climb there was a vast panorama of the hills to the south of Loch Tay. The road climbed to over eighteen hundred feet, and at the top was a dam with a sizeable reservoir behind it, still 2,100 feet short of the summit. The descent was via a bleak glen scoured by a rocky torrent that fed the Lyon.

We fished till about three in the afternoon and had a good few pearls, more than covering the expense of the Kintyre fiasco. Tired and hungry, we were heading for home when we met Donald, Pete and Tawser coming up the glen. They had cut new tangs, got a couple of hours' sleep at home, then set off to the Lyon. Asked why they weren't at work, Tawser admitted that they hadn't got back till four-thirty in the morning because Donald had gone right up the west coast to Oban before turning east. They were too tired to go into work.

There was a distinct coolness in relations between the two houses for the next few days, and Yeaman Street was unusually quiet. As friends of both parties, I was in an awkward position. Neil and I had to go into Perth with Mary to sell the pearls he, Davy and I had got at the Lyon, while Donald and Mary went separately.

The men had little to do with selling the pearls; in fact, they handed the bottle over to the two Marys. The night before they were sold, a clean, soft cloth was spread on the floor in front of the fire, and the pearls were emptied into a saucer with their water. On this occasion, Neil's Mary was preparing them. The pearls were taken from the saucer individually and wiped dry on the cloth. It was done on the floor because there was less chance of their escaping by dropping and rolling or bouncing under a chair. Small pearls still manage to spring from the cloth when it is stretched, and care has to be taken.

When they were dried to their natural shine, they were graded according to fineness. The very finest went into a matchbox first. This grade included large pearls with small imperfections such as fine drops that had a small brown patch on the sharp end. This did not detract from the pearl in a piece of jewellery because the fault would be hidden by the mounting. If there were a lot of pearls, perhaps the accumulation of several days' fishing for three or four men, an intermediate box divided the good box from the 'rubbish'. It contained good 'enders' – that is, half brown pearls with fine lustrous white ends. Also there would be brown-ringed barrels, brown-bottomed buttons and slightly lacklustre pearls of all types.

The rubbish box was not usually sold after one day's fishing but left for a week or two's accumulation to make it worth while. Teeth, vunks, enders and all other borderline stuff went in this box. As I mentioned, the jewellers sometimes found interesting challenges in the rubbish, and a good box had been known to fetch more than the better pearls from a good day.

We sat watching the sorting, reliving the day's fishing, each of us recalling from our own pearls where we had sat to open the shells they came from, or the precise spot where a good crook was lifted. Perhaps one stretch stood out as throwing a good bag of crooks, even though they might not have given the proportional amount of pearls. Our last real sight of the pearls would be when they were all dried and ready to go in their respective boxes, lying in a cluster on a piece of black velvet. When I see them like that, it seems a shame to have to drill them, or trap them, gripped by metal claws, in a piece of jewellery.

About nine-thirty in the morning we set off for Perth. Normally, Donald, Neil, the two Marys and myself would have gone, along with any youngsters who had managed to convince their mother that they were not quite well enough for school but could stand a trip to town with a few sweets and a bottle of lemonade thrown in. This time it was just Neil, Mary and I. Donald and his wife were taking the pearls he, Pete Bell and Tawser had got, another time.

First stop, as usual, was the premises of A. & G. Cairncross in St John Street. The two Marys dealt with 'Mr Alastair', who was in partnership with his brother, James Cairncross. If Mr Alastair was in, and other business permitted, the pearls might be viewed that morning. They were judged and weighed in groups according to shape and fineness, and it could be a long job when there were perhaps a hundred or more. The finest pearls are weighed on their own, and old scales are still used with the grain weights that are familiar to the fishers, despite the recent legislation imposing the metric carat on jewellers.

The shop was founded in 1869, a few doors from its present double-fronted premises, by the grandfather of the present proprietors, and his brother. Despite the 'Pearl Fever' of the 1860s, Alec and George Cairncross first advertised as watchmakers, and it was the present proprietors' father, James, who developed his fascination for freshwater pearls into an increasingly important part of the business around the turn of the century. James died in the 1920s, leaving the business in trust for his infant sons, who took up its running in the early fifties. During the thirties there was increased interest in freshwater pearls, and they continued to develop it after the war.

Today, freshwater pearls are hardly essential to the survival of A. & G. Cairncross, any more than they are to the very few other jewellers who deal in them. However, the Cairncross Brothers value them not just as providing a fair proportion of their income but as a draw which attracts customers to all the other beautiful things in the shop. Perth is a county town, and the shop attracts 'county' people and wealthy visitors, many of whom come to see something unique. The Abernethy Pearl is just that. Bill Abernethy got it in 1967. It is forty-four grains, half an inch in diameter, and is perfectly spherical. There have been bigger balls, and some would have had an equally good lustre, but the like of this pearl has not been seen in living memory. The others have gone into private collections or are mounted in jewellery and are no longer acknowledged as freshwater pearls. For what it is, it cannot be valued, and is therefore priceless. Formerly, pearls of this type would find their way into regalia, and indeed, the Scottish crow is said to contain such pearls. The age of the Scottish regalia makes it unlikely to have oriental pearls in it.

The Abernethy pearl is on permanent display in A. & G. Cairncross's, and it has long been our ambition to walk in one day, ask for the case containing it to be opened and throw down an even bigger one next to it. Donald's idea would not have been quite so mild. He wants to have the Abernethy pearl laid before him and break it with a hammer before showing his own.

While we waited for the pearls to be assessed, the ladies usually went shopping. With anything from fifty to 250 grains of pearls, at their estimate, fetching at least £1 a grain over all, the trolleys in the supermarket were filled to overflowing, then the clothes and second-hand shops were raided, with no worry about money. We men sauntered round the shops, drove the women to the next shop, went for a drink and bought tasty morsels or even whole cooked chickens while passing the time. The whole business had an easy, careless, holiday feel to it.

Returning to St John Street, we sat in the car, savouring the moment of topping up our wallets again when the ladies emerged from the door of the jewellers. We always had to guess what the pearls had fetched before they would tell us, unless it had been a little less than expected. After that it was home to a huge meal, followed by a quiet drink at 'The George' on an animated discussion on where we were going to fish the following day.

The advantage of selling to the Cairncrosses was that they took all the pearls we could give them, while some jewellers paid a slightly higher price, but the proceeds of a week's fishing kept them going for a year. Because they drilled and mounted the pearls themselves, on jewellery of their own design, the Cairncrosses took a wide variety of shapes and colours. Even some of the rubbish, which we could hardly imagine being of any use, suggested a design which the finished article more than justified.

Also, fishers were cordially and respectfully treated. Another Perth jeweller I dealt with very occasionally had a less flattering approach. A couple of times I met him in the street while on my way to his door. He would ask to see the pearls on the spot and bid me for them there and then, as if I were desperate for money because the pubs were open. He always spiced the deal by saying that, if I were to wait at the shop, he might be able to manage a slightly better price in half an hour. Sometimes he tried to beat me down by saying that the water had been low and that a lot of pearls had been forthcoming. Apart from Abernethy, my friends and I were in the water more than anyone, and certainly had more knowledge of what little was left in it than he did. As shells became scarcer, how much water there was had little to do with the amount of pearls taken.

Once, just before I went to America for the last (so far) time, I took him a fairly nice ten-grain ball. He rolled it round his palm as if it were a maggoty pea and told me he'd had a lot of that kind of stuff. At his derisory offer of £20, I went to Cairncross's and got double. Having fished full-time for seven years, I knew how often ten-grain balls would come up, and what even a slightly dull silver ball would fetch. A total of £55 for an afternoon at the Tay just before we went away was the kind of luck we needed.

An article I wrote about pearl-fishing included a photograph of some pearls with a caption* saying they were sometimes as valuable as oyster pearls. In the window of Cairncross's shop Neil and I once saw a pair of ten-grain balls we thought we recognized as our having taken from the Spey on consecutive trips. Mine was more blue than his, and they formed the central pair of a small but beautiful necklace of about seventy pearls. Alongside was a cultured pearl necklace with its largest pearls around twenty grains or more and with considerably more pearls in it. At £3,000 the river pearls were four times as expensive for less than half the weight.

* Their own caption.

14. Local Burns

Between trips to the Spey and other rivers, we worked our way systematically up the Tay above Aberfeldy, a part of the river now almost devoid of shells. The Tay was falling gradually, and the more inaccessible shells were coming within reach. Though an experienced fisher could still pick up a good few pearls in the shallows, most of the shells lay in deeper waters which divers had not yet plundered. Despite there being relatively fewer pearls in heavy streams and holes, weak shells from there, possibly containing pearls, were washed into the shallows by winter spates. A few years later, divers had all but destroyed these sources of replenishment.

One lovely June day, the weather and the call of the water got the better of us. It was too late in the day to go anywhere but the Tay or the South Esk, and I had a date that evening with the younger sister of a friend of the two Marys. Cancelling dates at a moment's notice, jumping in the car and disappearing, perhaps for days, was hardly the ideal basis for a 'meaningful relationship', but I thought that Nancy Paterson would know the ways of the pearl-fishers well enough. She probably knew them better than I did. While the two Marys smiled with benign self-satisfaction on this development, Neil and Donald found it a great source of amusement. I was acutely aware that they derived enormous pleasure from my discomfiture, particularly as entanglement with women had caused me, for the first time since leaving home, to have to explain my comings and goings.

I was unable to find Nancy to let her know we were fishing and had to leave a message. We picked up Gordon and headed up Strathtay. Just before Aberfeldy, where the river, the road and an abandoned railway line run side by side, there is a track leading beneath the railway with a bit of waste ground beside it. This is the 'Two Trees' camp, and here I saw a bow camp for the first time. A black stovepipe jutted jauntily from the roof, and a pack of squabbling children milled round an old pram full of sticks nearby. Further on, Donald spotted the 'chief of the tribe' from the camp as he called him.

'There he is! Deek him! How he struts, the cock tink!' he shouted excitedly and, rolling down his window, called, 'Aye, ged!'

The man certainly was strutting. So proud, he wasn't just erect but leaned backwards to counterbalance the swell of his chest.

We stopped two or three miles past Aberfeldy where the river and road were close together. Beneath the trees here, shells were already very scarce. My tangs were useless, and I had to cut another set, gashing my finger badly with the machete in the process. To get more shells we'd have to cross the river, which was nearly a hundred yards wide here.

We started at the head of a stream in calm shallows. Past the middle of the river the water crept up to the waist. Three quarters of the way over, it reached almost to the top of the waders and began to move with increasing speed. We had to stick together in case someone lost their footing on the slippy round stones of the bottom, inching forward with our tangs braced against the bottom on the downstream side. With low-slung, baggy, canvas waders, I didn't think I'd make it and tried to turn back. Face on to the current, the drag was worse. Desperately I dug my tangs into the bottom behind me. They slithered, then caught. The roar of white water under the trees just below drowned my thoughts. Side-on, I tried backing away from the deep part, and managed a few steps till it was easier to stand. Sidling upstream a little, I could see the shallows through my jug about ten feet ahead, but it seemed too deep between.

'What the hell,' I thought, 'I've fished without waders. Water won't do me any harm, as long as I keep my feet, and my head.'

I went straight at it and got over with only a slight wetting. The others were already fishing upstream under a belt of arn (alder) trees that overhung the water, catching at jerseys and hair and preventing our reaching the shells under the thickest branches. The difficult crossing and the distance from the town and the nearest bridge had protected the shells here while those by the road had been decimated.

We had a few pearls when we came out of the trees onto an open grassy bank where two youths were fishing for shells off the steep rocky sides. They wore no waders, their jugs were made of dried milk tins with the glass held in with candle wax, typical travellers' style, and their tangs were hastily made from knobbly sticks broken from the trees at the waterside. They would be thrown down when they finished fishing.

'Catbakers,' whispered Donald, using one of his vocabulary of derisory terms for bow-camp dwellers.' I bet they're fae that teepee by the railway.'

Gordon and I fished near them, reaching off the steep jumble of rocks thrown down the bank to prevent erosion and where the shells were hidden. One of them spoke to Gordon.

'Are you a MacPhee?'

Gordon shook his head in disgust. The very name was bad luck.

When Donald heard, he laughed and said, 'It's that bat's chin. Nae wonder he thought he was a MacPhee.'

Though I can recognize a 'bat's' chin, I can't really explain it. Hearing an unmentionable name did no harm as I got quite a few pearls from the rocky bank, despite a finger stiffened with congealed blood.

On the way back we cross at the place we used setting out because it gives confidence knowing we've managed it already. However, since I prefer having the current hitting my left side and holding the downstream side with my tangs in my right hand braced on the bottom, it was even harder on the return journey. (A day or two later the water was so low that we could cross almost anywhere and could park nearly opposite where we'd finished the previous time. We still had to walk a long way round the inside of bends. When the force of the water is on the outside of the curve, most of the shells, if there are any left, are there too.)

With a few pearls already in the bottle, we reached another strip of trees far from the road on the north bank, and any easy crossing from the south. A good sprinkling of shells sat high between rocks and weeds in a strip wide enough for two men to work side by side. By the time it ran out near the inside of the next curve, we had over fifty grains in the bottle.

Here I began really to become aware of the subtle difference that marked a bottom that could throw pearls, as distinct from that which merely supported shells. Neil and Donald's disproportionately large contribution to the pearls made it plain that there was still plenty I had to learn, and it had nothing to do with seeing donkeys or speaking about adders.

Further on, the confluence of the Lyon with the Tay barred our path. While the others looked along the near bank of the Lyon, I tried to cross. Typically, just a few yards from the far bank, a hollow in the shingle stopped me. Content with a good day, we walked back to a crossing through lush grass, full of wild hyacinth and red campion, bending before a scented breeze: a rustling breath of damp grass and water and, in my memory, haunted by the scent of flowers I never saw.

Many local rivers seemed to be in a state of decline, even to my inexperienced eyes. One day at the Lyon we walked several miles for a few shells, and very few pearls. We finished at Bridge of Balgie. The car was brought up by each pair of fishers driving ahead of the other and leaving it in sight of the river where they started fishing.

Donald, Neil and Davy were fishing deep pools near the bridge, and Gordon and I went downstream. I saw a shallow stream that resembled the one at Meggernie. It lay at one side of a series of gravelly islands where the river divided. On reaching it, I found it had the same bottom and the same type of shells as Meggernie. Gordon saw me lifting shells for all I was worth and joined me. We ran through it two or three times, and the tops of our upturned jugs were dotted with pearls. It was late, and we went back to the car. The others had got nothing in the deep water.

That was the last time we made much at the Lyon, apart from when Neil dived the pools near the bridge years later. Others brag that they've had good days fishing, but we discount it as idle boasting. All we see now are occasional travellers killing infant shells, as though they've forgotten anything larger ever existed.

The South Esk from below Cortachy, seat of the Earls of Airlie, down to Bridge of Dun by Montrose, was fished by us fairly frequently. One afternoon we had worked our way up from the bridge by Brechin and came on a little sandy 'stream' only inches deep, at the mouth of a burn. It was full of little crooks, many of which threw surprisingly large pearls. Big Davy was on his hands and knees as we raked through them with our fingers.

As we walked on, a farmer bellowed at us, and we left him fuming, ignoring him completely. That part of the river was jealously protected. One night Neil and I went to fish a muddy backwash near Brechin. We left the car at a bridge, and as we walked across a field, we suddenly heard a bellow from behind. A distant figure on the road gesticulated wildly. We'd nearly reached the cover of the woods by the river when a little Renault came bouncing over the bumpy ground and skidded to a halt beside us. The driver leapt out. I have no recollection of his face because it was so distorted by rage that, when the fit passed, only the first impression remained.

'Ye cannae gang in there. We're fed up wi' you tinks disturbing the pools and leaving deid shells stinkin' the place oot.'

'We'll no be near any pools, an' we throw the shells back in the burn,' Neil said in a level voice of reason.

'Och, ye aye dae damage. I'm seek o' it.'

I interrupted his tirade. 'What's the point of our doing damage? We'd never be able to fish the same river twice.'

Anger was replaced by cunning. 'I can mak' damage.' He basked in the glow of self-satisfaction.

I could scarcely believe what I was hearing. 'You mean you'd perjure yourself in court, just to get us into trouble?'

Neil had come to the boil. 'Listen, sooker, we're only wanting an 'oor, and we'll be awa'. Ye cannae stop us anyway.'

'I can stop ye, but if ye're only an 'oor or so, on ye gae.' In the face of Neil's mounting fury he became conciliatory.

We fished the backwash for an hour and a half, keeping on the move as the silt rose in clouds before our feet. As we finished the top of the stretch, the bottom was beginning to clear. We took pearls that fetched ten times our outlay in fuel. Now we'd be lucky to get three times the cost of getting there if we stayed all day.

15. 'Up North'

Most pearl-fishers are close-mouthed, some to the point of ignorance. Others are outright liars who send fellow fishers on wild-goose chases or brag useless rivers out of all proportion. To them, two or three pearls and a heap of 'dross' in the bottom of an aspirin bottle becomes a bottleful of pearls, and the bottle becomes a milkbottle in the listener's imagination.

The Davises weren't like that. They were more like the boys I fished with. They liked to talk pearl-fishing with other fishers and weren't afraid of mentioning rivers they knew. Half a dozen we've fished came from them, and a couple of them were as good as any we knew. Even at 1973 prices it was possible to make £50 to £100 in one afternoon at a good place.

One, a remote Sutherland river we don't fish often, nevertheless occupies a special place in my affections. Here I found the only pearl I've so far managed to have made into a piece of jewellery for my wife, one of the finest buttons I've found, set in an eighteen-carat gold ring like a delicate flower. It is unique, a one off, created by A. & G. Cairncross of Perth to my wife's description of what she wanted. Despite a generous discount, it was nearly two years before I could pay for it.

Perhaps for those to whom Watford is in the north, hearing us talk of 'going up north' might sound strange, but this river lay at the end of an eight-hour drive of nearly 250 miles to the north of Blairgowrie. Six of us (Gordon, Davy and Tawser came) left in the late afternoon. We usually set off at night, but this was the kind of place we needed a night's sleep to tackle. We went up the A9 to Inverness, then on to Dingwall. Past Dingwall we cut inland, away from the Cromarty Firth, and emerged high above the Dornoch Firth at a famous viewpoint of the northern hills. Following the

Kyle of Sutherland, the broad, quietly flowing outlet of the rivers Oykell and Shin, once great pearl rivers, we came to the dam at Loch Shin. Beyond it, the enlarged loch stretched to infinity in a calm union of water and sky.

Leaving the loch, a single track road led us north to Strathnaver. Eventually leaving all habitation behind, we drove for seven miles along the newly afforested eastern side of a shallow moorland valley, several miles in breadth. Not a light was visible across the great, twilit emptiness of bogland and heather to the west. At the foot of a low hill the road curved over a small burn near which were two buildings, an empty cottage and a pub! The Crask Inn is about five miles from its nearest locals at a shepherd's house on the far side of a little river that follows the road northwards. Three miles past that, the land falls away near the head of Loch Naver at the village of Altnaharra.

We stopped for a pint at the Altnaharra Hotel, then continued northwards over a little river and onto an even smaller road on which patches of grass could be seen between the wheel marks. Along Loch Naver side it was surprisingly light. An unnatural afterglow lingered beyond the appointed hour of darkness, and Donald detected a rise of flies on the mirror waters.

At last we reached the end of the loch and pulled off the road. While Neil, Gordon and I set camp and cooked eggs, beans and black pudding, Davy and Donald made for the loch with their rods.

Most sounds here were those we made. The occasional bleat of a distant sheep or the lost cry of a bird only emphasized our tiny presence. A strange thought occurred to me. This would be the kind of place to which I would come to die. Rooms are too much like coffins, or the grave itself, especially at night when the curtains are drawn. I have never really liked them. They are a refuge from the elements, rather than a place to spend one's life in. Even in a tent, death would seem to me to be a natural process and not to be feared. Walls, windows and roofs stifle this feeling of acceptance.

Donald and Davy returned with three tiny trout. We kept them in wet grass for later, and turned in. Next morning we cooked eggs and black pudding together. The result was a slimy omelette that looked as though it had a shovel full of coal thrown into it. We took the last four slices of bread, a tin of pilchards and an orange with us to the river. Three eggs and three four-ounce trout were left for evening.

The big river barring our way was low and easily forded. Old Davis had warned of a long walk to the good bits and that most them were 'boating water'. We knew the Davises seldom waded above thigh depth (often using only thigh waders) and had a folding canvas boat for anything deeper, so we were confident of being able to reach most of the bottom.

The river started unpromisingly rocky and fast-flowing, but even here shells were thick in the shallow, level parts between the rocky streams. They were mahogany beaks, typical of the north and western rivers, yet threw plenty of crooks and started us with some pearls before we'd even reached the pools Davis spoke of.

The sun shone down from a deep blue sky scattered with ruffles of white fluff that were too skimpy to cast a shadow. The forests by the river were too young to provide much shelter and lay beyond a seven-foot deer fence. Zigzagging in ankle-deep streams where the field of view was the width of the jug was hot work. We drank often from the river and emptied our jugs over our heads at times.

The river began to change. The short streams remained, though they were not so rocky, but the pools between were longer and deeper. Having started at seven, by about midday we were very hungry and gathered at the side of one pool for an opening and to divide the food. To our dismay, the bread and orange had disappeared from my bag, probably miles back, and only the tin of pilchards remained. One of the principal characteristics of the pearl-fishers was a lack of equipment, other than that essential for fishing, that is. No one had a tin-opener, not even a knife as a substitute. An outsider would think we'd never been away before.

'It'll hae to be the auld pearl-fishers' standby,' laughed Neil. 'Gi' us a stane somebody.'

He took an old penny from his pocket and began to hammer it through the lid with the stone. The contents of the almost unrecognizable can were poured onto the glass of an upturned jug, and we divided it into six and ate it with our fingers, oil running down our chins. The person to whom the jug belonged had to lick it clean.

As we fished further on, the pools got deeper and wider, which was odd because the river would obviously be carrying less water this far up. The shells were perfect: no longer mahogany beaks, they were jet black. Side on, they were almost egg-shaped instead of looking like stumpy bananas. Crooks were abundant: sometimes one in three shells was a crook. The bottom of the pools was pure sand, graded by the varying current into strips of fine and coarse, and rippled like a beach when the tide is out. The shells hid themselves deep in the soft bottom, so we lifted everything we could see, though in our excitement we missed quite a few, as always happened. We fished to the top of the waders, and sometimes a little beyond, and used the full length of our long sticks to reach further.

Two foresters spraying the trees came down to the water to fill their knapsack sprayer. They told us they were spraying against a moth caterpillar that made new shoots turn brown. Their spray was not a chemical but a bottle of caterpillars collected the previous year and left to rot into a stinking green sludge. This, in very dilute form, spread disease among the current season's caterpillars before they did too much damage. They also told us something more useful. There was a forest track we could use to get within a mile of the upper part of the river by car.

We fished on for a while and then, with a good bottle of pearls, started back to the car, now almost five miles away. Worn out and very hungry, we still forced the pace till at last the big river came into sight. We crossed, and by pure chance crossed our exact outward trail. The bag with the four slices of bread lay in our path. We fell on it, tore it into approximate shares and ate it dry, on the spot.

At the camp we cooked the three eggs together and divided by six. The tiny trout were cooked to a crisp at a fire of heather twigs, and snapped in two. Still ravenous, we jumped into the car and drove to the hotel nearly ten miles away, hoping for some sandwiches or a meal. There was nothing, hardly even a packet of crisps or peanuts. After an unusually quiet couple of pints, we went back to the camp without meeting another car on the whole road. About six-thirty, hunger overcame exhaustion. We rose and broke camp, packed the car and went by the foresters' route.

Seven miles into the forest we were on the point of giving up when, breasting a rise, we saw the river down a long slope of newly turned ridges of peat in which young trees had been planted. It was only a mile or so away. The 'convenient short cut' made us forget our hunger, and we set off down a broad firebreak. It was a lot further than it looked, and at the bottom of the break hundreds of drainage furrows crossed our path. The ditch and bank they formed sometimes had a combined height of almost three feet and was a formidable obstacle to us in waders. It was not so bad walking down them, but huge areas of them crossed our path diagonally. The return trip would be a test of stamina, starting with the seven-foot, barbed-wire-topped deer fence by the river.

Arriving at the river, we were unsure whether we'd fished that part or not and had to walk downriver till we were sure we recognized a landmark, of which there were very few. Some of the pools were too deep to cover completely by wading.

Gordon climbed out of one deep part onto a sandy ledge, then, with a yell, fell backwards down the bank. I could only watch, powerless, from the other side of the pool as he hung with his feet on the ledge, and his head beneath the water. He struggled up again. Laughing, he stood up, and all the water that the back of his waders had scooped ran down his back and soaked his trousers. Undaunted, he stripped to his underpants, put his waders in his bag and pranced along the bank with his trousers waving like a flag from his tangs to dry.

By an old meander loop, on a boggy piece of ground, was the only landmark, a black alder tree that the others called an 'arn'. It was the only native tree as far as the eye could see and had a huge, untidy nest in its sparse branches. We passed the tree, skirting the loop with its bottom of peat ooze of unknown depth, and a large bird fluttered into the water and flapped across to the other side. Another landed almost at our feet. From their size, dark eyes and wings that reached almost to the tip of their tails, they were young peregrines. Gordon risked the boggy water to return the first one to the same side as the nest tree. It sat back on its tail, wings outspread and one talon raised, and hissed at him. He caught it, but it got its head round and tore a flap of flesh back from his knuckle. We left eyasses worth £3,000 to an unscrupulous falconer, standing together at the bottom of the nest tree. The parent birds were never seen. The eyrie had not been occupied the last couple of times we have passed.

Further on we gathered at a pool that proved mostly too deep to fish, and had an opening. Tawser had a couple of nice pearls on his upturned jug that put my last opening to shame. I went down to the sandy ledge that was just above the water of the deep pool and looked in. Two shells sat side on to me by a big rock in about six feet of water. I sat on the ledge with my feet dangling over to get more reach. We used longer tangs in those days, and I was able to dislodge the shells, one of which I was sure was a crook, and drag them nearer. Once up, I found both were crooks. One contained two barrels about ten grains each, with identical thin brown rings round the middle.

Indescribable weariness made us like zombies. The car was a dot at the top of an inclined bog guarded by the deer fence. Tawser hung dangerously from the barbed wire at the top of the fence, swaying from one side to the other before almost falling down on the correct side.

Away from the river, the ground rose steadily. We had a choice of stumbling along the tops of crumbly peat banks or walking in the furrows, which was like wading through syrup. The last quarter of a mile of open ground got gradually steeper, and the car did not seem any nearer. Never slackening the pace, Donald, Neil and I left Gordon well back, and Tawser even further behind. We arrived at the car just in front of Davy, in a lather. Staggering from side to side, Gordon, then Tawser, arrived and fell on their backs. In a fumbling, staggering daze we took our waders off, with minor hindrances seeming insurmountable. There was no food, and the nearest shop was about thirty miles away. In blank resignation we sat in the car, barely able to rouse ourselves to open the gates that barred our way out of the forest every couple of miles.

We emerged from the trees onto the road and went towards the east coast instead of going back to Lairg. We'd put over twenty miles between us and the river when hopes were raised by the sight of a village. We passed through the straggling hamlet, too small to possess a shop, and barely raised hope sank. Then a shout rang out.

'A van! A mobile shop! Stop, ged!'

We screeched to a halt by the last house in the village and abandoned the car, doors swinging. Davy was first in and craftily grabbed something to eat, chewing at it as he waited to pay for it, before joining us for more. Each of us spent pounds buying whole fruit pies, large family-sized meat pies and pints of milk. Though we couldn't eat all we bought, it was good to indulge our fantasy appetites to the full.

Restored by the food, we stopped at the River Helmsdale a little further on. I put on the easy waders for a look in a nice corner, while Donald donned his 'twa scoppit' gamekeeper's bonnet and watched through my binoculars to make sure the fishermen nearby thought my activities had the approval of the water authority. It didn't work, and they came and told me to move on, which I did, only after looking at another bit right in front of them. A little further down I found a couple of shells near the roadside that looked good. We noted it as a possible and headed for home.

My share of that two days' fishing was nearly two weeks' wages to me. The pearls we got were worth nearly £200, and our contribution to petrol costs had been about £1 each.

16. Pearls and Berries

Summer seemed barely to have reached Scotland when the berry-time arrived. Apart from odd days snatched amidst picking, or long sunlit evenings at the Tay or Clova, fishing came to a halt for a month while the men supervised the picking of the raspberry crop from the six acres they rented from the Church of Scotland. Donald's low opinion of picking as a livelihood was accurate, but he changed his tune now their own berries were ready. As usual, at the high point of the season, when the berries turned the drills scarlet, the weather turned sour. Donald, Neil and I stood for three days in pouring rain, picking to clear the bushes before mildew set in.

When the sun came out, Shakum appeared. Where he came from nobody knew, though rumour had it that he was living in a cave on the west coast. He had a sunny face beneath a half-moon forehead of receding, mousy hair. Beneath a dirty fawn raincoat tied with a frayed rope was either an emaciated body beneath many layers of clothing or a few rags and a stout body.

Donald and Neil greeted him warmly and introduced me to him. The fact that he wore thigh waders beneath the raincoat on the warmest day so far seems hardly worth mentioning. He was thrown out of 'The George' that night because someone pointed out to the landlord that the coat and waders failed to conceal his lack of trousers. Donald tried to remedy this by getting him a pair of 'Big Dayser's' breeks. Dayser was twenty-six stone at that time.

'Been on the Brasso lately?' Donald enquired casually.

'Och, no,' Shakum replied in his soft, mild tone. 'They've put something in it an' I cannae tak' it. It made me see things that werenae there.'

'Peter kens a barry drink,' Donald managed to splutter between fits of mirth. 'Tell him aboot the birch sap wine.'

I explained how the birch trees were tapped in early spring when the sap was rising, which was mixed with other ingredients, and had reached the part about the three-month fermentation when Shakum stopped me. Disappointed, he said, 'I couldnae wait three months, ged. I thocht ye just put the pipe intae the tree an' lay down wi' the other end in your mooth.'

Donald and Neil hung on to the berry wire till they'd stopped laughing. 'Tell him aboot the nutmeg,' Donald panted, so I related the story of a girl who'd put herself in a state of semi-consciousness and delirium for three days by eating an ounce of nutmeg.

'That's mair like it,' Shakum beamed. 'I like a quick thing.'

A few days later, just after breakfast, my brother Jeremy arrived out of the blue. I told him to come in, in as surly a manner as I could muster, and he stayed for three weeks. During his stay, ostensibly to pick berries, Jeremy preferred to hang about the house with the older McGregor and McCormick boys who were trying to avoid work, and I was branded a traitor for picking berries with Nancy for a day on another farm.

The water had been high after the downpour in the peak picking time, and with a week's solid berries behind them, the men decided to have a day at the Spey. Though he had no waders and jug, Jeremy came with us for the ride. We fished between the bridges at Grantown-on-Spey and had a terrible day, though that didn't prevent our spending more on the way home than we'd earned. All day we were plagued by swarms of flies buzzing round our heads in the humidity that no doubt made us smell very attractive in our rubber suits.

We returned by the 'Auld Road' and stopped at Allargue for 'a pint'. Five hours later, at one in the morning, we came out to the car, but Donald had left his bonnet and went back for it. When he didn't reappear, first Davy, then Neil and Gordon went to look for him.

'I'll go and see what's happened,' I said to Jeremy, who was very tired. 'It's probably still going strong in there.' Before I knew what was happening, someone had put another glass of whisky in my hand, and things were back to square one. It was about one-thirty when we made our final exit.

I drove the car load of snoring, mumbling zombies over the empty moorland, fighting off sleep myself within the first five miles. The road gave little room for a lapse in concentration, and I kept going with a gigantic effort of will. High above Deeside, I stopped to relieve myself. A mantle of inky silence hung about the hunched shoulders of Lochnagar. The others crawled out into the cool night air. There was no need to seek cover for our activities. We just stood on the empty road under the stars like cattle.

The cool air was a brief respite. I was nodding again within a mile, and we still had forty-five miles to go. From Deeside to the Devil's Elbow was not too bad, but the Glenshee road heaved and humped and rolled the car in a broken cross-swell of hill and hollow.

We dropped Gordon off, then pulled into the yard in Yeaman Street at ten to three. Two sleepy figures dropped on the couch in Neil's living-room, and a smell of cooking came from the kitchen. Donald's Mary roused herself and went across to feed her man, and Neil's wife shot him a withering look as she disappeared into the kitchen.

'Nancy was along,' she shouted above clattering plates and pots. 'The pair lassie got wearied waiting. She went awa' home about midnacht. I dinnae blame her, ged, I'm seek o' it m'sel'. We've had the meat ready since the back o' echt.'

'You should know better by now, Mary,' I laughed, 'or are things worse since I came?'

'I dinnae ken, but there must be some attraction at that Allargue,' she probed, 'women, or dances, or something.' She finished loudly enough for Neil to hear.

'It's a wilderness, ged! The bar isnae half the size o' this room, and the only folk who come in are gamies, ghillies and fermers and the like. Ye cannae even get a seat.'

'Where dae their wives geng? Dinnae tell us they sit at hame like us,' came the reply from the kitchen. Mary came through with two steaming plates of stew, and Neil was a little more conciliatory while she held them out.

'The best thing I can dae, Mary, is tak' ye there, and ye can see for y'sel' what the attraction is.'

It was a scene that was no doubt repeated in the houses of all the pearl-fishers at one time or another.

We hadn't been to the Yorkshire Esk since our first look the previous year. The berries were almost over now, and picking was less frequent, so there was a two-day gap to fill. I was going out with Nancy the night before we left and wanted to get back before midnight as we were leaving at 4 a.m. to get a whole day's fishing on the first day.

Arriving back at Neil's at ten to three in the morning, I rolled myself into the sleeping-bag on the floor upstairs beside Jeremy. It seemed to be only seconds later that Neil's hushed call woke me. I was up instantly, dressing and trying to wake Jeremy while Neil was attempting to rouse Donald without disturbing the whole household. Jeremy seemed to have expired during the night, and I could only rouse him by inflicting painful gouges in his ribs with my toes. I went into the kitchen, and Neil thrust a fried egg roll into my hand and asked if Jeremy was ready. We ate standing up and were ready to pack the car after a quick wash. Davy Bell was always prompt. As soon as he saw movement, he came over and put his bag in the car.

Donald's house was in its usual turmoil. Everyone was awake, groaning and complaining at the noise and getting in each other's way. Donald wandered randomly with one sock on, a fried egg roll in one hand and a cup of tea in the other, roaring, 'Wha's awa' wi' ma sock, ged, an' whaur's the other wading boot?' He turned to me imploringly. 'Ged dear, what use would ane cut-off welly be tae onybiddy?' I shrugged non-committally and went to sit in the car with the others. Donald came out shouting back, 'Watch the baby, Mary. Dinnae gae mad in the shop.' We started the engine as he had got into his seat; then he leaped out again. 'Has anyone put my jug in the boot? Meat, ged! I've left my meat!' He disappeared into the house again and emerged a few minutes later with a bag of food, shouting more goodbyes.

At last we got away. Neil drove and Jeremy and I caught up on lost sleep. We passed through Edinburgh long before the rush hour and reached the border in two hours flat. Shortly after eight we were at the river, putting our waders on in a little track that forded the lower part of the mussel beds.

Neil and I went to the water, leaving Davy, Donald and Jeremy to take the car upstream and walk down to fish. We got shells right away. They lay thick in shallow streams: big black shells that led us on with promise of great, gnarled crooks and princely pearls. How we harvested. Great bags of shells were dragged to the bank. There was hardly a crook to be seen, and not a seed for the slaughter. Crossing a meander loop to avoid a deep, muddy stretch, we were confronted by the familiar red-faced bully.

'WHOTTAR YOODOONG HEEAH?'

'Pearl-fishing,' we said, thinking curiosity might deflect his wrath. No such luck.

'You people think you can march across other people's land and ruin their fishing.'

We ran through our well-rehearsed lines: 'You can't stop us fishing for pearls. There is no law against fishing pearls. There is a royal charter granting pearl-fishing rights to anyone, in any river.'

'You can't tell me you can trespass on private property looking for pearls. It's just not on. We get all sorts of people trampling about looking for mussels.'

'Ged! The carry-on for a' fish y'ed ever tak' fae this burn.'

Luckily for his blood pressure, the fisherman couldn't make anything of Neil's dialect, and we left him in the middle of the field delivering a dissertation on declining standards of law and order to some Friesian heifers.

We came on a long, dark pool. It looked too deep, but we slithered down the bank and touched bottom just short of the top of the waders. Clay from further up the dale silted the sandy bottom, and it was hard to see. We picked up half a dozen shells between us, four of them crooks. Our only pearls came from there.

'This must hae bin the guid bit,' Neil said with resignation. 'Nae shells here but cassied doon the way.'

Fishing on, we came on evidence of the others in the form of little depressions where shells had been lifted and clear sandy patches where their feet had disturbed the sediment that blanketed much of the bottom.

The others had fared a little better than we had. It was quite late when we met and, as usual, we'd not eaten since daybreak. Whitby, at the mouth of the river, was the nearest town, and we found a very good chip shop near the harbour there.

Restored in body by the food but troubled in mind by the lack of pearls, we went north into the gathering darkness. There were no other rivers south of the Esk on the eastern side of the country.

Finding a railway inn to our liking, we whiled away the evening there before pitching the tent a little further on. Although Jeremy hadn't been able to fish, he was enjoying himself nevertheless.

We'd just covered our expenses at the Esk and now decided to fish the little river in Northumberland that we'd been at the previous year on our way home from the Esk. Donald, Neil and Davy had already fished it in March, and Donald had taken an eighteen-grain ball from a long pool. He knew the exact spot by a solitary stunted tree growing by the bank. It had been so cold in March, with snow on the hills, that they had fished only the middle part of the river, and we walked a long way downstream to avoid that stretch. However, with so many people in the water, each man leapfrogging the others when he finished his bit, we soon covered all the fresh ground. Even Jeremy went in without waders, using a spare jug. Donald and I reached the pool where he got his pearl, which had been almost a centimetre in diameter.

As we neared the little tree, Donald fished more slowly, obviously hoping to repeat his previous success there. The bottom was sandy, with small stones, all covered with little weeds and grey-brown silt. The shells were large but so deeply buried that only a pale fawn slit betrayed their presence, and this closed when they felt the disturbance our approaching feet made. Opposite the tree I lifted a shell that was much fatter than usual. It was a crook, and a good one.

At the top of the pool we had an opening. I kept my crooks till last, and Donald drooled over the one from by the tree. 'Bound tae be pearl in there. What a crook!' He peered at it from all angles, trying to penetrate its secret without actually opening it. A little later he leaned over my bag: 'Ye havnae er ... opened that crook yet?'

When I prised it about half an inch, a bulging pearl sac could be seen, with a pale sheen glowing through the diaphanous mantle. As Donald started forward, I laid the shell aside with a sharp intake of breath, the way he did. To put him out of his misery, I opened it quickly and popped the pearl into his hand.

'It's a bonny ball, ged! Must be ten grain anyway.'

It was the biggest saleable pearl I'd had and was worth a day's pay for us on its own. In fact, I've never had a bigger ball in all the years I've fished. I've had 'fawns', a near miss and other shapes that were bigger. I usually get a large weight of pearls in smaller sizes, while someone else gets two or three larger ones.

After finishing we ate at the camp and went to the pub at the bridge again. They greeted us very hospitably and kept the place open an hour and a half past time, which didn't really help us on the three-hour drive home.

17. Jockey Matches' Burn

Tawser took time off from the cannery to go with us to a river his mother had mentioned: the Pollaidh. His grandfather, 'Jocky Matches' – so called from when he sold matches in the streets of Inverness as a boy – had rated this little burn in Ross highly.

Though not far as the crow flies, it is a tortuous road to Wester Ross from Perthshire. Long ago I'd painted landscapes from photographs of the west coast and had longed to see it. We went up the A9 to Inverness, along the Beauly Firth, then travelled north to Muir of Ord. I was amazed at the lush landscape near the Black Isle, especially after miles of hill and heather from Blair Atholl to Inverness. This northern garden countryside had wheat, potatoes, strawberries and raspberries growing in neatly hedged fields lined with oaks.

Crossing the River Conon, through Strathpeffer, still in farming country, we soon rose onto high moors again. Clear blue skies failed to alleviate the utter desolation of the dark waters of Loch Glascarnoch. The loch mirrored another, colder sky that I could not see above, a sky more befitting the grey ruins scarring the sides of the great, crumbling hills beyond. Amid muted greys, soft browns and sorrowful purples, the pebbles of the loch shore shone like distant daffodils.

There were few roads here. In over sixty miles between us and the north coast only two roads crossed the country from east to west, and apart from the coast roads, only two ran north to south.

The shores of Loch Broom, a sea loch, were verdant after the wilderness we'd passed through. Small fields dotted the flat, alluvial land leading down to the sea. Little whitewashed cottages dotted the green hills on the far side of the water on our left. Ahead of us, on the northern shoreline, stood the fishing village of

Ullapool, blinding us with its sunlit, whitewashed houses.

Stopping only to buy pies, we continued northwards past a couple of promising rivers. The landscape changed again. There was water everywhere. The hills were low, tortured, writhing shapes that forced the road into similar contortions. It skirted shapeless lochans, bogs, heathery mounds and huge rocks. Burns ran from one lochan to another with no regard for the direction of the sea. Ahead of us was a mountain larger by far than any of the other hills nearby, and yet the map contradicted this impression.

'Stac Pollaidh,' Neil indicated, as though sensing my interest. We passed beneath its southern flank. It was so weird and out of place that it dominated the whole area, despite being several hundred feet short of a couple of neighbouring hills. It was like a huge ruin, a vast, decaying fortress, its long ramparts cracked and riven, thrusting up defiantly through a mound of their own debris. It could have been a mesa from the Arizona desert set in a land of lochs and burns. From the west it assumed a new identity: end on, it was a steep-sided cone.

We came to a small bridge over a rocky little river. Neil pulled onto grass by the water, and we put on our waders. I was busy taking a photograph when a car pulled up and the driver jumped out. We knew what came next.

'You can't fish here. This is Inverpolly Estate fishing.'

'We're no fishing, we're looking for pearls,' Donald replied firmly.

'You can't touch THEM either. We put the shells there.'

'You must hae done it a lang time ago,' retorted Neil. 'They've been there since the Ice Age.'

'There's only a certain Perth man allowed to fish here. If you try, I'll get the police. I'm leaving a man to watch you while I'm away.'

'Auld McCann fae Perth fishes here,' Donald said when the car had gone.

Neil, Donald, and Gordon went below the bridge, while Tawser and I fished above it, watched by a man sitting on a rock by the water. We found the river bottom eroded as though a terrific spate had torn it up. An occasional shell sat up high in the coarse gravel of the bottom. We lifted a couple. They were huge mahogany-coloured 'beaks', of little use for finding pearls. I realized the bed of the river had been dredged by mechanical shovel to make it more suitable for salmon-fishing. Our watcher spoke.

'This is a bit stupid,' he said apologetically. 'That idiot goes off half cocked as soon as anyone goes near the river.'

'What's the fuss about?' I asked, wondering why there was so much bother in this wilderness.

'Part of the estate is a nature reserve, and they've started a fish farm.' He kicked his heels, embarrassed by his task, and we fished on right in front of him but soon ran out of shells and went down to join the others. The other three were approaching the car.

'Have you been put off?' Tawser asked.

'No, we fished it tae the sea. It's less than half a mile,' Donald replied.

'Aye, there were a couple o' deep bits wi' black shells in them, but we couldnae reach the half o' them,' Neil added. 'D'you boys hae any luck?'

'A puckle red beaks,' Tawser answered, disappointed.

'That moicher's coming back,' Donald hissed as a car pulled up, blocking us in.

As well as the man who'd already threatened us with the police, there was another man and two ladies in the car. As Donald walked towards the car, the driver said something to him and he went berserk.

'Fool's bastard! Ye cannae stop us fishing!' He ran at the car, stuck his head into the driver's window and hurled a stream of abuse at the man, who tried to make off, but Donald ran alongside with his head in the window, still roaring, till the car outpaced him.

The estate man stopped at what he thought was a safe distance, got out and shouted, 'You'd be better at the Kirkaig. There are plenty of shells there.'

'That's in the journal,' I told the others. 'It's the next river north of here.'

We resolved to look at it before going south again, and kept our waders on for the fairly short drive. It lay at the bottom of a steep hill and was spanned by a girder bridge.

'That's nae use, ged. It's a nuclear vortex.' Donald threw his arms in the air and turned on his heel. Neil and I stopped to read a sign at the beginning of a riverside path. The path, it said, led to the Falls of Kirkaig, about seven miles upriver.

'There could be shells above the falls,' I suggested.

'Aye, but Tawser'd never walk it, and Donald's got the burn doomed.'

Donald sat resolutely in the car, determined not to go anywhere, so we went back to Ullapool for fish and chips. Tawser bought a box of kippers from one of the quayside sheds, and we headed southwards, this time keeping to the west coast road. Typical of the north at that time of year, it was still fairly light at midnight when we came down to Gairloch. From one hill we could see the whole range of the western hills against a pale green afterglow.

Near Gairloch there was a little river. We turned down beside it and put the tent up on a lawn of sheep-cropped grass beside the water. Lulled by the sound of running water and the soft breeze gently flapping the tent, sleep came to us almost immediately.

At first light Tawser, Gordon and I crawled out of the tent, and Donald and Neil emerged from the car. Donald kindled a fire, its smoke lost in the pale grey mist hanging over the river.

'You and Peter havnae seen the shells in this burn,' Neil said with a grin to Tawser and me. 'Lift a bag while we're makin' the meat. They're lyin' in millions, but ye wouldnae get a crook for Britain.'

We put our waders on and, shuddering slightly in the early morning chill, waded out bent over our jugs. Thankfully the water didn't come above the thighs, and despite the poor light, we could see the bottom was carpeted so thickly with shells that I lifted one accidentally while steadying myself with my stick.

'Put on some o' my kippers,' Tawser called to Gordon and Donald at the fire, and the smell of them sizzling in the pan soon brought us to the bank with a bag of small, narrow, red shells.

We scanned the bag of shells quickly. There were no crooks, and the smell of kippers was driving us mad. I threw most of my shells back. By the time we left the little River Kerry, Tawser's kippers were all finished.

We went up Kerrysdale past the loch the river ran out of. Lack of roads to the south forced us eastwards to the shores of Loch Maree. We met the loch at its broadest point, where a cluster of wooded islands lay becalmed, walled off by the green flanks of a line of misted peaks rising straight from the far shore. At the head of the loch we were able to take our intended south-westerly direction again, climbing between great, clouded hills and descending to the sea at Torridon. Ten miles without seeing a living soul and barely a sign of habitation. Conversation had lapsed till we saw a postman at Torridon. Finding there were other people left on earth seemed to break a vow of silence among us.

The road mimicked the convolute shoreline of Upper Loch Torridon, and the sea lay like a vat of mercury in the bowl of the hills. Beneath the lid of leaden mist, the silence could be felt above the noise of the car. At the head of Loch Shieldaig we had to veer south because there was no road to Applecross, our destination. The Davis family of Dornoch, a northern tribe of pearl-fishers, had told us there was a pearl river in the Applecross Forest.

In sight of the sea again at the head of Loch Kishorn, we drove up a steep corry on the north shore, between two huge buttresses of rock, Meall Gorm and Sgurr a Chaeorachain. The bends in the road became sharper and steeper, with no room for mistakes. Tawser hung on and tried not to look as we climbed into a pall of mist and drizzle, with a last glimpse of Kishorn framed between the vertical sides of the corry and the cloud base. On top the road levelled out, passing over two thousand feet, then descending more gradually into Applecross. Half way down, on our right, we saw the broad glen where the river flowed. To the west, the bulk of Skye hovered between cloud and sea.

Unbelievable as it was to us, the tiny hamlet supported a pub, and Donald suggested we ask there about fishing. The rest favoured fishing without permission: asking only drew attention to our activities. We were told to try the last place we needed to go to: the estate office. 'You gae in,' Donald urged me. 'You can speak like a brute.' This was his term for well-off, well-spoken types. Neil and I went in, and the secretary phoned the factor. We already knew things were slipping away from us.

'Is himself there?' The secretary's accent had a lilting, soft, almost Irish quality. We stood waiting for the inevitable. 'He says the tide is on the turn, and the fish will run on the rising water, so he'd prefer it if you didn't disturb the pools just now.'

We went through the motions of acquiescing and jumped in the car and made straight for the river, despite Donald's attempt to spread alarm and despondency. At a bridge just beyond the village the river didn't look good. We drove up the glen some way, but the road took us away from the river. A small burn parallel to the river had a perfect bottom, but by now Donald's persistent carping had put everyone off, and we turned back in sullen silence. By the time we returned to Kishorn, the sun was shining on a silver sea. We got to Loch Carron to find a sign at the junction saying that Stromeferry was not operating.

Neil groaned. 'Ged! We've tae gang recht tae Strathpeffer, doon Loch Ness and back up Glen Moriston, just tae get over there.' He pointed to the other side of Loch Carron. The round-about route would cover over one hundred miles to reach a river ten miles from where we stood. We'd have been as well to go home from Loch Ness.

We started out to the east. The sun blazed down on the whitewashed seafront of Jeantown, mocking us in defeat. I drew Neil's attention to what I thought was a road on the south shore of the loch.

'There's nae road there. That's the railway line tae the Kyle o' Lochalsh.'

'I can see that, but there's a road as well,' I said.

'Aye, there is a road, but it's a dead end.'

'It seems to go right along,' I finished lamely, realizing the map agreed with Neil.

At the head of Loch Carron a road branched right over the River Carron to Attadale. A new sign read 'To Stromeferry.'

'You're recht enough, there's a new road,' Neil cried with obvious relief, and we swung over the bridge and down the other side of the loch.

As we went over the high ground between Loch Carron and Loch Duich, a vast panorama of hills and lochs spread before us beneath a canopy of broken high cloud. Ahead, across the Sound of Sleat, was Skye; on our left the long finger of Loch Duich pointed towards a perfectly proportioned range of hills.

'Where are we?' I asked as we stopped to take a photograph.

'No far fae Kyle o' Lochalsh,' Neil answered. 'Those are the Five Sisters o' Kintail.' He pointed at the hills I'd photographed.

We crossed over the end of Loch Long and came to that most Scottish of castles, Eilean Donan. At the top of Loch Duich were three rivers, one of which we were going to fish. The River Shiel ran through a deep glen below the Five Sisters. Crossing Shiel Bridge, we parked in a layby that had been part of the old road.

'We'll tak' the dinghy wi' us, Neily.' Donald had been keen to try the dinghy on a little loch that the river passed through.

It took only a couple of hours or so to fish the mile to the loch. Only Tawser got anything worthwhile. He had two huge 'barrels' with thin brown rings round them, worth over £20. Donald had carried the dinghy for a mile and spent half an hour blowing it up and getting ready for the water. It took him two seconds to see that there were no shells in the quiet water of the loch, and another half an hour to deflate it and carry it back to the car.

The way home lay down the Great Glen, then up Glen Spean to meet the A9. The railway through Glen Spean runs in a gorge beside the river like the Canadian Pacific line through the Rockies.

Twilight faded as we wound along the shores of the seemingly endless Loch Laggan. It was dark when we reached the A9, with fifty miles still to go, and well after midnight when we got to Rattray.

18. The Season's Close

Our final major venture of my first season as a professional fisher was a failure on a magnificent scale involving so much expense for so little return that I would really like to pretend it didn't happen. However, as we did it again, and again, and again, there is no escape. If I ever recount the story of our later adventures, the truth will be less sore, blunted by early confession.

We got hold of a paper on the North American distribution of the pearl mussel. This, and a massive crook from another species of mussel that Andra sent from Ontario, fired us up to go to Canada, and go we did. It cost us about £750 to lift about two dozen pearls mussels and hundreds of assorted hechans, and to come home after three weeks with £18 worth of pearls. Unfortunately, as I have said, the story doesn't end there. After 'The Ultimate Gooser', we made between us three more sorties to North America, each one involving greater expense than its predecessor, yet none of them producing any greater return than the first. Total expenditure was over £6,000 for less than £50 worth of pearls. But what good times we had.

If all this was past history, or perhaps water under the bridge would be more appropriate, then all recriminations could be laid to rest with it. The really sad thing is that we still believe that somewhere in the vastness of Canada or the USA there is an unfinished river as good as a virgin Spey would have been to the first fisher who laid eyes on it. To rub salt in our wounds, Donald has a small bottle of pearls fished by a totally inexperienced middle-aged woman he and Mary met by a river in which we could find nothing of note.

It was now late September, and the trees were turning and the first frosts had come. The three of us were strangely affected by what we'd seen and done, and couldn't shake off a feeling of unreality. There was only one place left so late in the season, and that was the Spey. While we'd been away, nobody else had been up, so we had no idea what state the water was in. I realized that, without Donald and Neil, few of the weekend fishers ever budged from Rattray. Only a couple had cars, and some of them didn't like to venture away on their own.

We set off 'blind', not knowing if the water was too high or 'dirty' (brown with peat). As soon as we saw the river, Donald pronounced it 'pure brown an' a mile high' and could scarcely be prevented from turning back there and then. 'Ye neednae care. Ye'll no see a hait. It's like lava, ged.'

Neil drove on till we came to 'the concrete brig'. Here the river divided, one part rushing round the back of a small island and full of black 'mooths', as Donald called the shells here, and the broader part rattling over shallows to the bridge. The 'mooths' were no good for pearls, but a shallow stream beyond the island was, and there was a similar stream on the east bank.

The water was very peaty, and high. There had obviously been a dry spell followed by a short, sharp rainstorm. It was cold after the soft Canadian conditions, with temperatures that seldom fell below the highest we have ever encountered in Speyside. We lit a fire at Donald's request to 'ken'le a low'* (as in cow) and walked up to it each time we had an opening. Fishing shallow water near the side when the river was high meant few shells. This was because, as well as being fished out by travellers without waders, these parts are exposed at low-water levels.

With only one nice button of about four grains in my bottle, we crossed back to the side where the car lay, using the bridge. None of us wanted to attempt the quick water and the slippy round stones of the crossing upstream we usually used. The high brown water prevented our seeing our feet in water more than thing depth. Under the trees that shaded the west bank, slanting sunlight arrowed through the overhanging branches and made blinding shafts of light in the peat suspension in the water. The shadows were left in dark contrast, and it was impossible to see the shells.

We left early and drove slowly home down the Auld Road. We

* Kindle a fire.

were each lost in our own thoughts: a grey dawning of the realization that things could not continue. Rivers, shells and pearls were a finite resource that was diminishing rapidly. Even the serene autumn weather seemed to hasten the close of the season. Down through the whispering tide of trees that swept up to the bare moorland slopes above Strathdon, our quiet reflection was uninterrupted till Allargue came into sight.

For once, we went in almost from a sense of duty. They'd be wondering how we'd fared in Canada. On the way to the door it felt to me as though this was to be my last visit. All the usual keepers and stalkers were there: Geordie Chean, Alastair Nairn, Dunc and Ian Fraser, whom we could never tell apart, even though they were not twins. From behind the bar, Archie Stewart looked up in surprise and shouted through to the kitchen: 'Mary! The boys are back!'

Mary came bustling through from the kitchen, dusting flour from her hands, and we were bombarded with questions.

'Have ye bin up by? Far aboots? Not back at the Spey surely? How did ye get on o'er the water?'

It was good to hear their voices again after the stony silence of the journey down, and, to my surprise, I realized I'd missed them. At the end of the tiny bar, the postcard we'd sent from a place that was just a dream now looked mutely down.

'Drappy soupy, boys?' Mary asked as Archie gave us our first round on the house.

Warmed by a bowl of 'kail' and a few nips, the inexplicable sense of loss that had haunted us since our return began to ease. We didn't stay very late but went home in a better frame of mind than when we'd arrived. The forebodings of the poor day's fishing left us, and we regained our belief that things would always be so.

We fished the Deveron and the Don a couple of times that autumn and had few pearls, but of good size and quality, particularly some good buttons. When we had a poor day or the weather was dull and cool, depression returned, and we felt the whole country was worn out.

Later, in October, it was cold and frosty, with clear blue skies. Though the days were shorter, we were glad to leave the water before the frost regained its grip. Perhaps the colours in the hills appealed to the painter in me, or the strange beauty of that autumn was new to my eyes and impressed itself on my memory. Whatever the reason, it has stayed with me. The cobalt blue skies of day softened towards evening, and in the faded hills ultramarine pools of shadow filled and deepened. Against the darkness of the forests and rocks, sunlit silver birches slowly dripped their flakes of gold on the russet pile of the carpet of heather.

I was content. Lying back in the car, I let it wash over me. Only pearl-fishing produces such sustained contentment. There are moments of satisfaction in other things, but even intense concentration on painting and music failed to absorb sufficient mental *and* physical energy, seldom leaving me more than half satisfied.

The passing of the season of pearling was tinged with sadness. By next spring Nancy and I would be married. Neither of us was very demonstrative, and we had not talked of the event in so many words, but it somehow came to be understood. My friends and I had talked of the kind of life we each envisaged for ourselves, long before pearl-fishing turned dream to reality for me. Some girls said they found the ideas 'absolutely fascinating' (as they beat a hasty retreat). I made no attempt to pursue them, instinctively reading the thoughts behind the words. Nancy seemed to have few illusions about this life, and knew my dissident partners, perhaps better than I did.

Though our marriage was still more than three months away, we should have been a lot more worried than we were. We had nowhere to live. Nancy's father wasn't able to help. One of Nancy's brothers and a younger sister still lived with him. There was little money in the bank, and no prospect of a job for the winter. Despite the uncertainties, I could scarcely tear my eyes from the fading glories of the present season to gaze ahead across the wasteland of winter to a vague and distant future.

On 11 November 1973 Donald, Neil, Davy Bell, Gordon Wilson and I went to the Spey. Despite the sunshine, the frost had scarcely lifted. In the shadows it lay like fine snow in the bleached grass. We lit a succession of fires to heat our frozen hands, legs and feet. Hands hung from sleeves like dead trout. The water pressed the waders so tightly against the legs that it destroyed the insulation value of layers of socks and trousers and constricted the circulation. Twenty minutes between openings was all the body could stand, and there was so little feeling in the legs that it felt as though the dead, stumbling appendages that could be seen through the jug were artificial limbs. A diet of around seven thousand calories a day was needed to combat the simultaneous rigorous exercise and loss of body heat. The chip shop in Grantown must have done some heavy out-of-season trade.

It was almost dark when we reached Allargue that night. On the way down, we spoke of incidental matters. Though we all knew it, nobody wanted to admit the season was finally over. At last Neil said: 'I doot-a-doot that's it for the year, boys.' From their berries and pearl-fishing, Donald and Neil had enough money left to sit tight for some months. They had 'cutting out' and 'holing' (thinning raspberry plantations and digging young canes) on piece-work if they needed extra money. I'd never done these jobs (though I'm more than adept at them now) and didn't see myself surviving on them, let alone saving for marriage.

There was no point in going back to Camberley just before getting married, with no job waiting there either. I didn't want to impose on Neil and Mary without, at least, the means of paying board. Nancy's brother-in-law got me a job with him, labouring on the oil pipeline. The pay was 57 pence an hour, but by working seven twelve-hour days and several nights in a week, it was possible to earn sufficient to save money quite quickly.

The prospect of escaping the miserable grind of the pipeline to go pearl-fishing again in the spring shone like a wreckers' beacon before me, tempting me to pack up before Christmas. I hung on through the coldest November in living memory. While we slept on the formica-topped benches in the pipeline test wagon, the outside temperature fell to twenty-one below, and the ice creaked and groaned after slack water in the tidal reach of the River Earn.

During a lull in the work at the River Earn crossing, where the pipe bored beneath the ice-encrusted banks, the sandy bottom showed clearly at low tide. I took a jug and tangs from the wagon and put on thigh waders. The tidal mud was frozen and I walked easily out to the bare sand, finding a couple of shells right away. Before the tide began to rise, I'd lifted about a dozen. The fresh-fish smell of them set me longing for an end to this terrible winter, and the day we'd jump in the car and go out to the abandoned slate quarry above the Tay Valley, where ash saplings grow straight and true, and cut a new set of tangs to mark the start of a new season.

An Epilogue of Sorts

We feel no shame for the hedonistic approach we had to our profession but have been forced to recognize that we are an anachronism, a tribe of twentieth-century nomads who reaped a harvest they had not sown. My feelings, and probably those of my friends, when we set off for a river, were the same pangs of exhilaration and anticipation that gnawed at my innards as I lay in bed as a child, desperately awaiting the dawn of Christmas Day. To have had the same feeling 'going to work' defied the grim reality of a thousand Monday mornings.

Even near the close of a fruitless day's fishing, when the last glimmer of hope has been doused by a frozen, rain-sodden weariness, a couple of nice pearls from the last bag of shells can send you down the road in a state of exultation. To have found peace and deep contentment beyond the extremes of physical hardship, exhilaration and despair we endured is not the paradox it seems. Prospectors, mountaineers and athletes reach these goals by the same route. Pearl-fishers had the proud independence common to those who share hardship or danger. I never imagined I'd share such unself-conscious kinship, and now I fear its coming loss.

Even when the day's fishing was over, the journey home had its pleasures. Lying back in the car, tired and content, gazing out at the great empty land, bathed in the pastel shades of evening sun or cowering blue-black beneath the lash of ragged clouds, it felt so good to be alive. We had a little bottle of pearls in which were condensed many miles of driving, walking, fishing and all our hopes. We knew that we had taken a living where others saw only rock and water, and could come back and do it again. There is no such hope in us now. Each of us is becoming trapped in circumstances beyond our control, yet we cannot face normal life, seeing no solution there.

There are few openings for men aged between thirty-five and forty-five whose only experience is clinging to the edge of ruin by combination of cunning and self-reliance. The number and diversity of jobs we have tackled are too long and boring to relate. The best of them were tolerable, and some were even more lucrative than pearl-fishing. A few were sufficiently absorbing, for an hour or two at a stretch, to keep me from wondering if it was nearly time to go home. None of them made me regret the coming of evening. I never lost my appetite for breakfast in the excitement to get to work in the morning. If any of us bothered to wear a watch in the river, we looked at it in the hope that there was time to get a few more pearls before dark.

Though the halcyon days of pearl-fishing are over, we cling pathetically to the wreckage, hoping to be saved by a new source of pearls. More than once, each of us has spent his last penny, and a good few more, chasing rumours and scraps of information across the rivers of five countries. Total ruin is an old friend of ours. Sometimes I think that publishers would have accepted our story out of charity if they understood the purgatory of winters spent thinning raspberry plantations on piecework, but it may have tempered the will to succeed.

I suppose that to have made a spectacular change of direction instead of staying on the path of least resistance, and to have gone ahead with deliberate disregard for the consequences, in the face of dire warnings, might have been enough. To succeed at it for a number of years was the greatest good fortune that could have befallen me. It rekindled feelings that I assumed withered with the passing of youth.

To say I'd no regrets would be a lie, especially as some of my friends are doing so well in their chosen fields, while we slither rapidly downhill. We mourn the loss not just of what we did but of what we were. Many people, even the successful, envied our unfettered existence, yet the publication of its story may still fail to vindicate what some friends and family see only as wasted years. However, the intense interest of many curious strangers and the encouragement of friends have reawakened our appreciation of what we had, and led me to set down the events of days, the like of which we shall not see again.

In the river, or round a fire in the evening, wherever it may be, pearl-fishers are figures in a landscape, belonging there as a much as tree or hill. River and road are their element. Their affinity with them is that of the gypsy with the open road or the sailor with the sea. There can be no surprise at meeting a seaman in any corner of the ocean, and he is neither stranger nor foreigner till he sets foot on dry land. To these people, the tourist is the antithesis of the traveller. They are to be pitied: lost souls who wander, gaping vacantly on synthetic cultures or longingly at a reality they cannot enter. Some strive so energetically to belong that, like little boys stoning a drifting toy boat to bring it back to shore, they succeed only in driving their objective even further from reach.

I suppose we too carried our small world with us. Yet often, far from home after days of hard fishing and driving, we'd stumble on an inn, park our battered car and go inside, dishevelled and apparently destitute, and spend freely. Assorted strangers gravitated to our circle as though hoping to glean some of the romance they ascribed to our way of life. We have been the recipients of great hospitality, we have been thanked, and even apologized to, for time spent satisfying the curiosity of our hosts. It was our pleasure anyway. Many seemed comforted by the idea that people like us survived against the odds in an otherwise grey world of conformity. They could go on believing that cowboys still drive cattle across the Great Plains and that middle-aged, middle-class men, sick of commuting, can run away to sea. Nearer home, visitors to Scotland who fell in with us felt that they had caught, and held, something of the reality of a Scotland that had eluded them in the tartan-filled gift shops of Pitlochry.

How can we abandon such a life? We see nothing that can take its place. Nothing that we have done, or may yet do, can prevent us from thinking of ourselves as anything but pearl-fishers. An actor may fill time as a waiter without considering himself to *be* a waiter, even if years drag by between parts. We too live on hope. Our hope is that one day we will find another river as good as the Spey was, but one that nobody has fished before us. We know it will not be found in this country.

I very much doubt that we can learn to exchange independence, uncertainty and excitement for subjugation, security and boredom. Throw in money and we'd spend it all in futile efforts to buy back what we'd lost, but I feel we could not bite life to the core as we did when snatching our living from the brink of disaster.

One thing that could be said with certainty is that if one of us had come into a substantial sum of money, some of it would have been set aside for us to search for new pearl rivers, and if we'd found them, this manuscript would have been tossed aside and never finished.

Appendix: Pearl-fishing Beyond Britain

As my friends and I fished for pearls in several other countries over the following seven or eight years, I think it is worth mentioning the fisheries of these, and some other countries. Many of these fisheries depended on the same species of mussel and contained valuable lessons for us.

Most of the mountainous regions of northern Europe give birth to pearl mussel if not pearl-bearing rivers. In Hungary, Romania, Bulgaria and parts of Russia, pearls seem to have been exploited for the adornment of peasant costumes, marriage headdresses etc. rather than for the creation of jewellery.

Many regions of what now comprises East and West Germany produced freshwater pearls, but the Bavarian fishery is one of the largest and most interesting. It was so interesting that my friends and I were tempted to try fishing there despite its being against the law to tamper with the mussels, and in the face of a warning from a German conchologist 'to avoid dealings with policemans'.

From at least the late seventeenth century, the Bavarian fishery was run to a definite policy of conservation of stocks coupled with controlled cropping, in total contrast to the relative anarchy of the rest of Europe's pearl industry. An eighteenth-century book on aquatic life describes the issuing of pearl-fishing licences, records of pearls taken from each river, and the enforcement of quotas. Attempts were made to establish the pearl mussel in rivers which appeared suitable but had not been naturally colonized. To us barbarians, the quotas seem very strict. Certain smaller streams were allocated to three fishers for three days, then were left 'fallow' for twelve years! Pearls taken were put in three grades of fineness and weighed. The number and weight of each type were entered in records which still exist. From these records, my friends and I are pretty certain that a lot of pearls were siphoned off for private sales.

The Bavarians were the only fishers (as far as I can ascertain) who used a special tool with which to open the shells without killing them. It was placed between the valves and squeezed like pliers, but opened instead of closing. It could be locked to prevent the shell closing during the search. Seed pearls would be noted and the shell marked accordingly and returned to the water, or, more likely, taken to a stream near the fisher's home. The descendants of these 'nest egg' colonies can still be found in hamlets in the forested side valleys along the Regen Valley. Further natural colonization has taken them up into the forests that close off many of these valleys, a habitat they probably occupied before their pearls were of interest to the first settlers.

My friends and I often wondered what the Bavarian pearl-fishers were like. With their licences, quotas and written returns, they sound more like a branch of the civil service and bearing as much resemblance to Neil, Donald and me as the Roman troops would have done to the wild tribes that harried Caesar's search for pearls in Britain.

In Luneburg Heide, pearling was controlled by the Dukes of Brunswick Luneburg. The fishery of Hesse was the property of the Crown, while in Fichtelgebirge wealthy landowners dealt severely with trespassers on the mussel beds they owned, even in the twentieth century. However, when these restraints were removed, plundering drastically reduced the mussels everywhere, and the pearl mussel now appears in the German 'Red Data Book' of endangered species.

In Bavaria today, a high degree of local awareness of the state of the pearl mussel (which we came up against while there), backed by strongly enforced laws protecting the species, must bode well for it. According to the latest information, Bavarian rivers contain 130,000 individuals, eighty-six per cent of the total estimated German population of 150,000. The remainder are divided between two small, declining remnants of the Hesse and Luneburg Heide fisheries.

The Scandinavian countries were once a very important source of pearls. Sweden, with its longer, less steeply falling rivers, and the lower-lying lakes and rivers of Finland were probably more fertile than Norway's plunging torrents. In 1971 a Swedish jeweller, who seems to have ceased trading, was paying 4,000 kroner for 'fine pearls'. A rough estimate would place this at around £15 per grain, roughly ten times what we were getting. A report by the freshwater institute at Drottning, Sweden, said that pearl-fishers were still operating up to at least 1960 and that there were large mussel populations in the Parlhalven River (Pearl Haven) at that time.

Regulation of water channels between lakes in Finland and pollution in the south of the country have badly damaged mussel stocks. Overfishing too has helped to restrict the mussel to a few rivers in the far north which are not likely to be polluted by boats or industry. Acid rain may be their downfall.

The small Breton fishery in France has been fished to extinction, and that of the Vosges has suffered the same fate. Of the Spanish and Portuguese rivers, little is known. There is no record, as far as I know, of pearls having been fished in the rivers of the northern mountains which contain pearl mussels.

We, and the travellers who went before us, obviously had more in common with the American pearlers. At the height of the pearl fever, they lived in riverside camps and were described as 'easygoing, fun-loving people who worked hard all day and liked to relax in the evening round camp fires, dancing and singing to the music the banjo'. Well, I ask you, does this sound like the American of the 1860s? Ten years as a pearl-fisher qualifies me to criticize this account, which has obviously got mixed up with a report of a church picnic outing. Reading between the lines, I see a shanty town inhabited by a bunch of hard-bitten, get-rich-quick types and well-worn women preying on any fisher who came on a good pearl bed.

'Relaxing in the evenings round the camp fire ...' We've only to look at the Gold Rush towns to see what that involved. Kegs of vicious rum and rotgut whisky swallowed in an orgy of wild dancing would lead to a lucky fisher's being relieved of his pearls while he lay blottered in the debris of the spree. An innocent third party would probably get stabbed as a result; then there would be a lynching.

I'd like to make it clear that my friends and I do not fit this caricature of the American pearl-fisher, quite.

Strangely, pearl fever hit North America about the same time as it swept Scotland (about 1860). The tale which surrounds its beginning is of the 'big one that got away' type. In 1860 Paterson, New Jersey, was a little town on the Passiac River, about fifteen miles west of what is now the Bronx. Today, Paterson is the northwestern extremity of a conurbation connecting Newark, Jersey City and New York City. Joseph Quackenbush (an unlikely name), a shoemaker in the town, went fishing in nearby Notch Brook and brought home a 'mess of clams' to fry for supper. Having fried them (the story gets a bit far-fetched here), he discovered a pearl of over four hundred grains, totally ruined by hot fat. On hearing of this, a friend went to the same place and found a ninety-three grain pearl of the finest quality. He sold it to Tiffany's of New York for several thousand dollars. (Donald's wife Mary took a pearl to Tiffany's once and was told not only that did they not deal in freshwater pearls but that they never had.)

Here are all the ingredients of a pearl-fishing tale: precise names, dates, size of pearls, price obtained, mixed with such obvious exaggeration and blatant disregard for facts that I'm amazed it got into print. Such tales belong in a book of pearl-fishing legends. This one has several weaknesses. Over four hundred grains is a ludicrous size for a freshwater pearl. To miss such a pearl, which would be about an inch in diameter, while 'shucking the mussels into a pan' would be highly unlikely. In any case, clam dishes utilize only the adductor muscles, and the rest is waste. Pearls do not occur in the muscles and would not find their way into the pan.

It is likely that pearls found in Notch Brook were from the pearl mussel, *Margaritifera margaritifera*, as they occur in the Atlantic drainage from Pennsylvania (Lat. 40 deg. North) to the north coast of Labrador. As the 'fever' spread, other species of shells in other river system were found to produce fine pearls in abundance. One of the most prolific was *Quadrula undulata*, though its common name, the Blue Ridge, is more easily called to mind. Others were the Pancake, the Butterfly, the Maple Leaf and the Hackleback. Incidentally, the Blue Ridge got its name not from the Blue Ridge Mountains of Virginia but from a faint blue line round the sharp edge of the shell.

The Mississippi and many of its tributaries formed the largest freshwater pearl-fishery in the world, and until then, apart from early Spanish incursions and occasional Red Indian fishers, it was completely untouched. Among the Mississippi's tributaries, the Black River and its affluents, the White and Arkansas Rivers, the Ohio River and the Tennessee River (now virtually all lake, confined behind strings of power dams) all produced fine pearls. Further north, at Prairie du Chien and in the Wisconsin tributaries of the Mississippi, beautiful pearls of rose pink were found.

American fishers seemed to have had no grasp of factors that related to the incidence of pearls. One contemporary writer reported that the fishers simply worked their way upriver, finding that 'one part had an abundance of pearls, while in others, many tons of clams had to be raised to find any pearls'. It is likely that the large, muddy rivers which are typical of the interior of the country prevented the fishers' observing any difference between one bed of 'clams' and another. The deficiency was made up in part by the number of shells that could be taken.

The American fishers used a kind of spiked roller trailed behind a boat. Called a crowfoot drag, it worked on the principle that spikes entering the slightly open valves of the clam would cause it to close on reflex and become trapped on the roller by their own muscle power. A two-man team could lift a ton of clams a day, while two of us might manage a quarter of that with stick and jug. To us, half the excitement was seeing what you were getting.

The origin of the crowfoot drag is interesting to speculate on. In the forested hills of the eastern mountains, rivers and creeks were the only breaks through which a wagon, or, more commonly, an ox-drawn log sled, could pass. Some of them still served this purpose in the early years of this century. Crudely trim a pine log, leaving a lot of stumpy branches protruding, then drag it down a mussel-bearing stream and some shells will stick to the finer twigs. Cut all the branches to the same length and sharpen them to fine points, drive a spike into the cut ends so that a pair of ropes may be used to pull it along, and you have a crowfoot drag. Later, purpose-built metal rollers bristling with spokes superseded the log.

Pearl fever caused the market to go mad. In Canada, someone reputedly sold a fawn ten-grain ball for $1,500. Rivers and fishers gained reputations on the strength of such occurrence. It is small wonder that we made little of our four attempts to find a new Spey in the USA and Canada. It was not important that some of the American pearls were huge. If a burn here throws pearls, there is a chance of a big one sooner or later. Meanwhile, the 'sugar and tea' pearls mounted up till they outweighed the odd big one. Pushing through virgin forest wearing body waders in temperatures of nearly a hundred degrees, already sweating from the thought of meeting a black bear face to face and armed with a set of tangs, was not the way to do it. We cannot afford to sit by a Canadian burn for weeks to get a fifty-grain ball, however exciting it might be. We should be hauling in at least fifty grains of smaller pearls each, every day.

There has been a steady decline in American fishery since the early years of the twentieth century. The pearl button industry took many tons of Mississippi shells until pearls became merely a by-product. West coast abalone, and plastic, superseded freshwater pearl buttons, and the last part-time button pearl-fishers on the Mississippi ceased operating in 1960, one hundred years after the Notch Brook finds set pearl fever sweeping the country like the plague.

Index